Experiments for Chemistry 1010

Southwest Tennessee Community College

Matta I Wilbraham I Staley

CENGAGE
Learning™

Australia • Brazil • Japan • Korea • Mexico • Singapore • Spain • United Kingdom • United States

Experiments for Chemistry 1010:
Southwest Tennessee Community College

Matta | Wilbraham | Staley

Executive Editors:
 Maureen Staudt
 Michael Stranz

Senior Project Development Manager:
 Linda DeStefano

Marketing Specialist:
 Sara Mercurio

Senior Production / Manufacturing Manager:
 Donna M. Brown

PreMedia Supervisor:
 Joel Brennecke

Rights & Permissions Specialist:
 Kalina Hintz
 Todd Osborne

Cover Image:
 Getty Images*

* Unless otherwise noted, all cover images used by Custom Solutions, a part of Cengage Learning, have been supplied courtesy of Getty Images with the exception of the Earthview cover image, which has been supplied by the National Aeronautics and Space Administration (NASA).

For product information and technology assistance, contact us at
Cengage Learning Customer & Sales Support, 1-800-354-9706

For permission to use material from this text or product, submit all requests online at **cengage.com/permissions**
Further permissions questions can be emailed to
permissionrequest@cengage.com

ISBN-13: 978-1-111-00449-1

ISBN-10: 1-111-00449-8

Cengage Learning
5191 Natorp Boulevard
Mason, Ohio 45040
USA

Cengage Learning is a leading provider of customized learning solutions with office locations around the globe, including Singapore, the United Kingdom, Australia, Mexico, Brazil, and Japan. Locate your local office at:
international.cengage.com/region

Cengage Learning products are represented in Canada by Nelson Education, Ltd.

For your lifelong learning solutions, visit **www.cengage.com/custom**

Visit our corporate website at **www.cengage.com**

Printed in the United States of America

Contents

Why do chemistry courses have laboratory programs? One reason is that you learn some skills only by doing them. Laboratory work also gives you the opportunity to handle chemicals and to observe for yourself the physical and chemical changes discussed in lectures. You have a chance to put into practice the time-honored methods of science: making observations, taking measurements, recording data, and drawing conclusions from the data. Many students find laboratory periods welcome interludes in days filled with reading and lectures. They consider the laboratory a place to use their hands for a change, to hone their powers of observation and logic, and to get to know other students. Best of all, these benefits result from doing work that can be fun.

To get the most from your laboratory experience, read the experimental procedure and do the prelaboratory quiz before coming to the laboratory. Follow all directions carefully, and consult your laboratory instructor if you have any questions concerning a procedure. *Safety in the laboratory is essential.* Organize your work in the laboratory to make most efficient use of your time. A reaction that requires boiling for 1 hour, for example, should be started as soon as the laboratory session begins, not when you have less than 1 hour left. You will work by yourself unless otherwise directed by your instructor. *As you make observations and measurements, record them neatly and clearly on the report sheets, not on bits of scrap paper that are easily lost.* Remember that your grade will depend on your reported results.

Everyone who works in a chemistry laboratory must respect the need for safety. It is your responsibility to know the safety rules and to practice them at all times. A chemistry laboratory should be a safe place to work—not only for you, but for all the other students in your class. Most accidents in chemistry laboratories are the result of

1. Doing unauthorized experiments
2. Failing to read instructions carefully
3. Handling hot glassware and other equipment carelessly
4. Subjecting glassware to too much pressure
5. Using the wrong technique for inserting glass tubing into rubber stoppers
6. Not wearing safety glasses
7. Not listening to the precautions given by your instructor

Learn and observe the following safety rules and laboratory procedures:

1. Wear approved safety glasses or protective goggles in the laboratory at all times. The laws of most states require that you wear eye protection while in the laboratory. Prescription glasses are usually considered adequate; contact lenses are not.
2. Wear a laboratory apron or other protective clothing. Do not wear your best clothes in the laboratory. Clothes with short sleeves are preferable to those with long sleeves; loose and floppy long sleeves must be secured or rolled up. Shoes must be worn in the laboratory at all times. Long hair must be pinned or tied back, especially when you are working with flames.
3. Do not eat, drink, or smoke in the laboratory. Wash your hands immediately after leaving the laboratory.
4. Never taste chemicals in the laboratory.
5. Check the odor of a chemical or a gas evolved by a reaction by cautiously wafting the vapors toward your nose with your hand. This technique will be demonstrated by your instructor.
6. Know the locations of fire extinguishers, fire alarms, emergency phones, eyewash fountains, safety (deluge) showers, and other safety features in and near the laboratory. Be certain that you know how to use them.

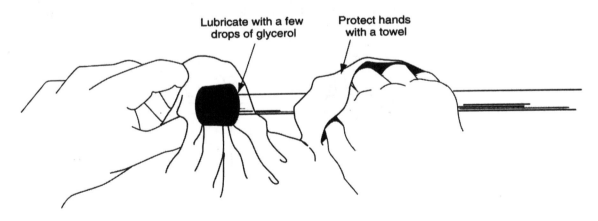

Lubricate with a few
drops of glycerol

Protect hands
with a towel

Figure 1 Correct procedure for inserting a glass tube into a rubber stopper.

7. Never begin your experiment unless the instructor is present. Never work alone in the laboratory, and never do unauthorized experiments. Read each experimental procedure carefully before coming to the laboratory. Pay particular attention to any cautions that are given.

8. Report all accidents, no matter how slight, to the instructor immediately. If you require medical attention, another person must accompany you to the health service.

9. Use the fume hood when doing experiments that involve irritating or toxic chemicals.

10. Most liquid wastes can be discarded in the sinks and flushed down the drain with water. Liquid wastes that emit toxic or irritating vapors must be disposed of only in the sinks in the fume hoods. Flammable solvents and certain other chemicals must be discarded in specially marked containers. The crock on your laboratory bench should be used for all solid wastes—broken glass, filter paper, paper towels, water-insoluble chemicals, and used matches.

11. Read the labels on reagent bottles carefully before using chemicals. To avoid contamination, never return unused chemicals to the reagent bottle. To avoid waste, do not take excessive amounts of reagents. Never put a pipet, spatula, or dropper pipet into a reagent bottle; instead, pour some of the reagent into a small, clean, dry beaker and use that as your supply.

12. When diluting acids, *always* pour concentrated acid slowly into water with a stirring rod to help to dissipate the heat generated. ***Caution:*** *Never pour water into concentrated acid.*

13. To insert a glass tube or a thermometer into a rubber stopper, wet the tube with water or glycerol, wrap the tube with a cloth, and then push it gently into the hole in the stopper with a turning motion (Fig. 1).

14. Never use an open flame when flammable liquids are being used in an experiment.

15. When dispensing solutions, never place the stopper from a reagent bottle on the bench; otherwise, the reagent may become contaminated. The stopper may be held between the third and fourth fingers of the right hand as shown in Figure 2. Always return stoppers to the correct bottles.

16. When heating a liquid in a test tube, never point the open end of the tube toward yourself or another person.

17. Hot glass looks like cold glass. Put hot glass in a safe place to cool.

18. Never leave a lighted burner unattended. Before leaving the laboratory, check to see that all gas and water outlets are turned off.

19. Be neat in your work; clean up spills and broken glass immediately. Leave your work area clean at the end of the laboratory period, and return special items to the side benches or storeroom.

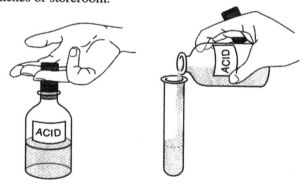

Figure 2 *Correct procedure for pouring a solution from a reagent bottle.*

Accidents happen no matter how careful people are in the laboratory. It is important, therefore, for you to know the location and use of fume hoods, fire extinguishers, fire blankets, the eyewash facility, the safety shower, and the emergency phone. Your instructor will describe the use of these facilities. If an accident occurs in the laboratory, you should be ready to help. The proper responses to common laboratory emergencies are as follows:

1. *Chemical splashes into eye.* Flush the eye immediately with large amounts of water, and continue the flushing for several minutes. If possible, a second person should assist the victim by holding the eyelids open. Contact lenses must be removed as soon as possible to ensure thorough washing of the eye. The victim should be taken to a doctor as soon as possible.

2. *Chemical burns.* Wash the affected area with plenty of water, and scrub gently with soap if the skin is not broken. The victim should see a doctor as quickly as possible. The doctor can treat the burn most effectively if you are able to supply the name of the chemical that caused the burn.

3. *Thermal burns.* Cool the burned area by immediately applying cold water or ice to reduce the pain and facilitate healing. The victim should be taken to a doctor as soon as possible. Application of petroleum jelly to a burn is *not* recommended because the doctor must remove the jelly before administering treatment.

4. *Fires.* If hair or clothing catches on fire, *do not run* because running fans a fire. Drop to the floor and roll to smother the flames, and shout for help. If another person is the victim, get a fire blanket to smother the flames or, if a deluge shower is nearby, help the victim to use it. A small fire in a reaction vessel may be put out by smothering with a damp cloth or with a portable carbon dioxide extinguisher—the type usually found in chemistry laboratories. If you have never used an extinguisher before, however, an emergency is not the time to practice. You may cause the fire to spread. Leave the task to the laboratory instructor, who has had experience in extinguishing fires. **Caution:** *Never direct the jet from a carbon dioxide fire extinguisher onto a person's face;* it could cause asphyxiation or frostbite. If a fire cannot be extinguished quickly, leave the laboratory, and call the campus emergency services immediately. In a smoke-filled room, crawl on the floor to the exit. *Do not* reenter the laboratory.

5. *Cuts.* Allow minor cuts to bleed for a short time, wash under cold running water, and then go to the health service for further treatment. Deep puncture wounds and serious lacerations require immediate medical assistance. Control the bleeding by applying pressure with the finger tips while waiting for the doctor to arrive.

6. *Toxic gas inhalation.* Remove the victim to a ventilated area and loosen clothing around the neck. Get medical help immediately.

Most of the equipment needed for the experiments in this manual is in your locker (Fig. 3). Equipment not in your locker but needed for certain experiments is located on the side benches in the laboratory (Fig. 4). At the beginning of the laboratory program you will check the equipment in your locker and replace any broken or cracked items. The contents of a typical check-in card are shown below:

LOCKER EQUIPMENT

Locker Number _____   Combination _____

Quantity	Item, Size	Quantity	Item, Size
1	Ceramic plate	1	Pair safety goggles
1	Beaker, 100-mL	1	Pipet bulb
2	Beakers, 250-mL	1	Screw clamp or pinch clamp
1	Beaker, 400-mL	1	Spatula, scoopula
1	Clamp, buret	1	Sponge
1	Clamp, ring stand	2	Stirring rods and policemen
1	Ring for ring stand	10	Test tubes, 13 × 100 mm (small)
1	Porcelain crucible and cover	6	Test tubes, 20 × 150 mm (medium)
1	Dish, evaporating	1	Test tube, 25 × 200 mm (large)
2	Dropper pipets	1	Test tube brush
2	Flasks, Erlenmeyer, 125-mL	1	Test tube holder
2	Flasks, Erlenmeyer, 250-mL	1	Test tube rack
1	Forceps	1	Thermometer ($-10\ °C$ to $110\ °C$)
1	Funnel, 65-mm	1	Tongs
1	Graduated cylinder, 10-mL	1	Triangle
1	Graduated cylinder, 25-mL, with guard	2	Watch glasses
1	Graduated cylinder, 100-mL, with guard	1	Wire gauze
1	Mortar and pestle	1	Wing top

I hereby accept responsibility for equipment in Kit Number _____

Name (Print) _____ Student No. _____

Address _____ Phone No. (____) _____
 (Street) (City) (State) (Zip)

I have read and understand the laboratory safety rules.

_____   _____
(Sign)   (Date)

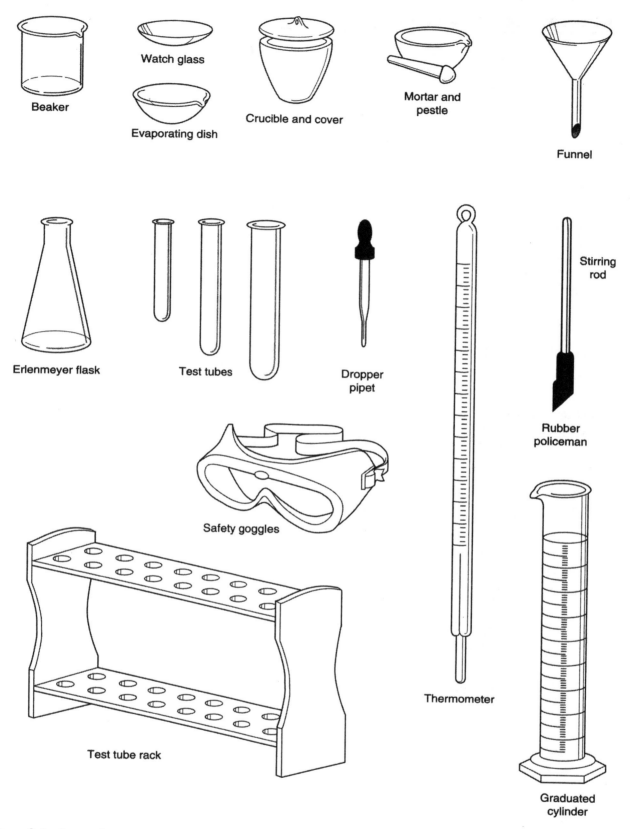

Figure 3 *Locker equipment.*

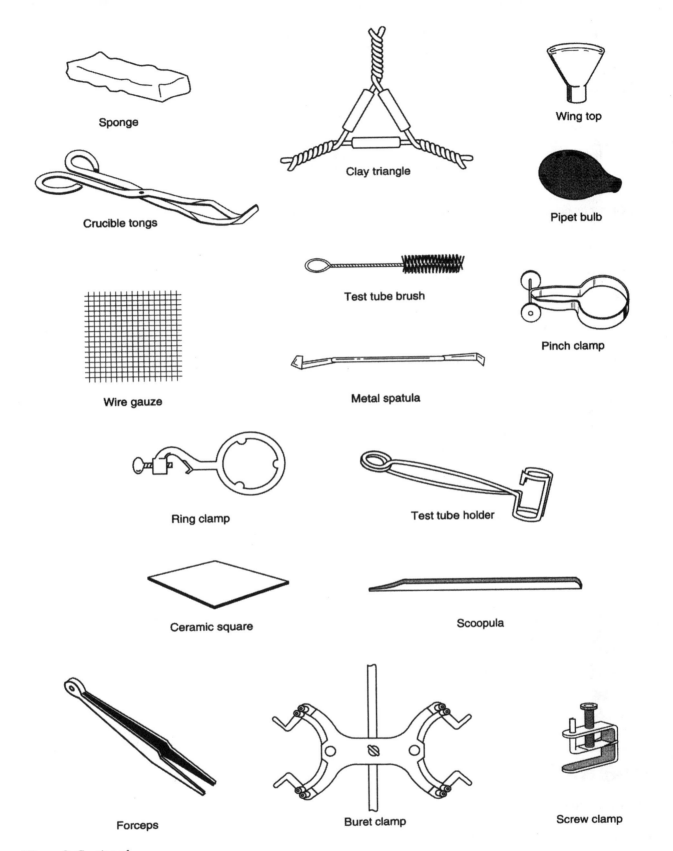

Sponge

Clay triangle

Wing top

Crucible tongs

Pipet bulb

Test tube brush

Pinch clamp

Wire gauze

Metal spatula

Ring clamp

Test tube holder

Ceramic square

Scoopula

Forceps

Buret clamp

Screw clamp

Figure 3 Continued.

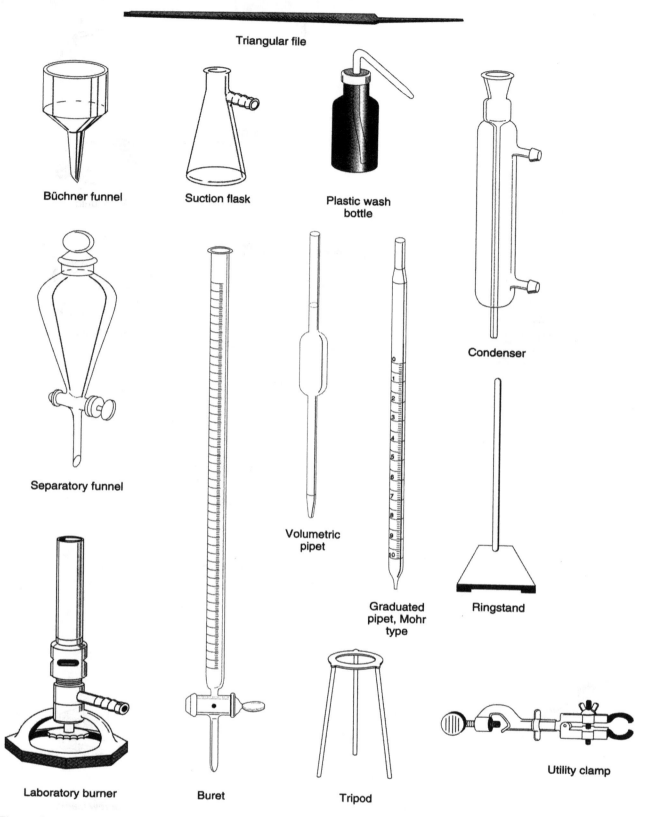

Triangular file

Büchner funnel

Suction flask

Plastic wash bottle

Condenser

Separatory funnel

Volumetric pipet

Graduated pipet, Mohr type

Ringstand

Laboratory burner

Buret

Tripod

Utility clamp

Figure 4 *Equipment available in the laboratory.*

Laboratory Techniques

The best way to become familiar with the equipment you will use in the chemistry laboratory is to handle it yourself. In this experiment you will learn how to adjust the laboratory gas burner, heat liquids, do simple glassworking, handle liquids and solids correctly, and filter a mixture.

Experiment 1.1 The Laboratory Gas Burner

Hypothesis The temperature of a burner flame can be controlled by adjusting the ratio of gas to air in the mixture to be burned.

Objective To learn to operate and use a laboratory gas burner.

SAFETY PRECAUTIONS	• **Wear safety goggles at all times while in the laboratory.** • **Long hair must be pinned or tied back and loose clothing secured when you are working with flames.** • **Keep flammable substances away from open flames.** • **Use tongs when handling the hot evaporating dish or copper wire.**

Materials and Equipment Paper matches, straight pins, copper wire, laboratory burners, rubber tubing, tongs, and evaporating dish

Procedure Laboratory gas burners produce various kinds of flames when different mixtures of gas and air are burned. The two most common laboratory gas burners are the Bunsen burner and the Tirrill burner. Both burners have adjustable air vents. The Tirrill burner also has a gas control valve in its base (Fig. 1.1).

Examine your laboratory burner. Observe how the air vents can be adjusted. Connect your burner to the gas supply with a short length of rubber hose, and close the air vents. It is usual to light a burner with the air vents closed. Turn on the gas and light the burner. (With a Tirrill burner, the main gas valve should be fully open, and gas flow to the burner is regulated by the gas control valve at the base of the burner. With a Bunsen burner, gas flow to the burner is controlled by the main gas valve.) The flame you get when the air vents are closed is called a *luminous* or *cool flame* (Fig. 1.2a). It is seldom used for laboratory work. Using a pair of tongs, hold an evaporating dish in the upper part of the luminous flame for 10 to 20 seconds and examine the surface of the dish.

Open the air vents slowly to admit air to the flame. Air drawn into the burner tube by the rapidly moving stream of gas mixes with the gas before entering the combustion region at the top of the burner. As air is introduced, the appearance of the flame changes dramatically from a sooty, luminous yellow to an almost invisible, nonluminous blue (Fig. 1.2b). Regulate the flow of air and gas to give a steady flame that extends about 6 to 8 cm above the barrel of the burner and has a sharply

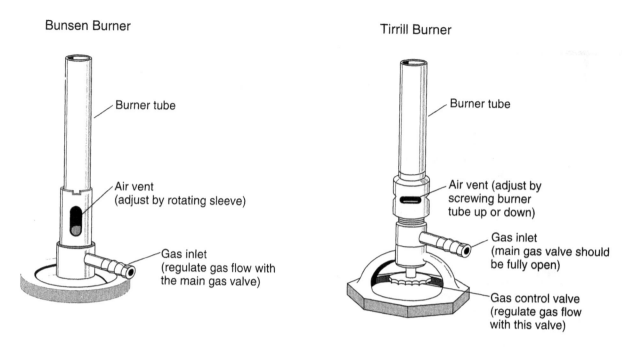

Bunsen Burner

- Burner tube
- Air vent (adjust by rotating sleeve)
- Gas inlet (regulate gas flow with the main gas valve)

Tirrill Burner

- Burner tube
- Air vent (adjust by screwing burner tube up or down)
- Gas inlet (main gas valve should be fully open)
- Gas control valve (regulate gas flow with this valve)

Figure 1.1 *Laboratory gas burners.*

defined blue inner cone. Holding a 10-cm piece of copper wire with tongs, insert the wire into the flame just above the top of the barrel. Lift the wire slowly upward in the flame, and hold the end of the wire in the hottest part of the flame, at the top of the inner cone, for about 30 seconds.

The interior of the inner cone (Fig. 1.2b) is unburned gas. To demonstrate this, turn off the burner without adjusting the air vents. Insert a straight pin through the stem of a paper match just below the match head, and hang the match in the burner tube as shown in Figure 1.3. Turn on the gas, light the burner, and note what happens.

You can adjust the intensity of the blue flame by changing the gas flow and air vents simultaneously. You will learn how to control the burner flame by trial and error. For most laboratory work, you should adjust the burner so that the flame is free of yellow color and free of the roaring noise caused by admitting too much air.

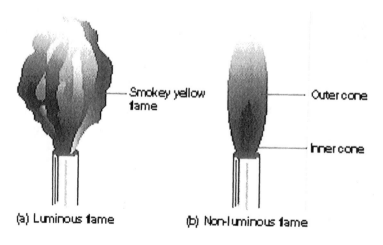

- Smokey yellow flame

(a) Luminous flame

- Outer cone
- Inner cone

(b) Non-luminous flame

Figure 1.2 *Burner flame characteristics.*

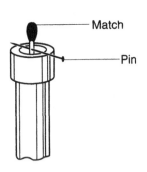

Figure 1.3 *Placement of match in burner tube.*

If the gas flow to the burner is too great or too much air is permitted to enter the vents, the flame will separate from the tip of the burner, burn noisily, and eventually blow itself out. To remedy this situation, you should reduce both the gas flow and the airflow to achieve the desired flame intensity.

Occasionally, a burner will "strike back," and the gas-air mixture will burn inside the burner tube. When this happens, the burner is noisy, and the burner tube becomes very hot. You should turn the gas off immediately and allow the burner to cool before you attempt to relight it. ***Caution:*** *Never leave a lit burner unattended. Always turn the burner off at the main gas valve when you have finished using it.*

Material Disposal Your instructor will tell you how to dispose of the materials.

Experiment 1.2 Heating Methods

Hypothesis Many laboratory procedures call for the safe heating of liquids.

Objective To learn correct and safe procedures for heating liquids in the laboratory.

SAFETY PRECAUTIONS	• Wear safety goggles at all times while in the laboratory. • Long hair must be pinned or tied back and loose clothing secured when you are working with flames. • Keep flammable substances away from open flames. • Use a test tube holder to hold test tube in the flame. • Use beaker tongs when handling the hot beaker.

Materials and Equipment Matches, laboratory burner, medium test tube, test tube holder, 250-mL beaker, ring clamp, ring stand, wire gauze, test tube rack, and tap water

Procedure **A. Heating a Liquid in a Test Tube.** Adjust the burner to give a gentle blue flame. Grasp a test tube, one-third filled with water, with a test tube holder. Hold the test tube in a slanting position in the flame, and gently heat the tube a short distance below the surface of the liquid (Fig. 1.4). ***Cautions:*** *Never point the open end of the test tube you are heating toward yourself or anyone working nearby. Never heat the bottom of the test tube.* Shake the tube gently as it is being heated, and bring the water to a boil. After the water has boiled, place the test tube in a test tube rack to cool.

Test tube

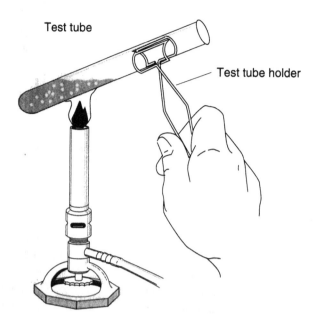

Test tube holder

Figure 1.4 *Heating a liquid in a test tube.*

B. Heating a Liquid in a Beaker. Fasten a ring securely to a ring stand. Place a 250-mL beaker, one-third filled with water, on wire gauze resting on the ring. The wire gauze should be positioned so that it is in the hottest region of the burner flame for the fastest heating (Fig. 1.5). For a slower rate of heating, reduce the intensity of the burner flame. ***Caution:*** *Never heat plastic beakers or graduated glassware in a burner flame.*

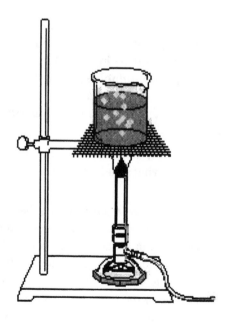

Figure 1.5 *Heating a liquid in a beaker.*

Material Disposal   Your instructor will tell you how to dispose of the materials.

Experiment 1.3 Glassworking

Hypothesis   Glass flows when it is heated.

Objective   To be able to do simple glassworking.

SAFETY PRECAUTIONS	• **Wear safety goggles at all times while in the laboratory.** • **Long hair must be pinned or tied back and loose clothing secured when you are working with flames.** • **Keep flammable substances away from open flames.** • **Be careful when you pick up pieces of glass; hot glass and cold glass look alike!** • **Place pieces of hot glass on a square of wire gauze to cool.**

Materials and Equipment   Glass tubing (6 mm), glass rod (6 mm), matches, triangular file, burner, rubber tubing, wing top, and wire gauze

Procedure   **A. Cutting Glass Tubing and Glass Rod.** Place a piece of glass tubing on a firm surface. Using a single firm stroke of a triangular file, make a deep scratch on the glass about 20 cm from one end. Grasp the glass in both hands with the scratch facing away from you and both thumbs directly behind the scratch. Push firmly with the thumbs, and pull with your fingers. The glass should snap with a clean break (Fig. 1.6). A drop of water on the scratch gives a smoother break. Be careful with the cut ends of the glass because they are sharp and possibly jagged. *Caution: Do not attempt to break glass with an outside diameter greater than about 6 mm.* Using the same procedure, cut a 20-cm length of glass rod and another 20-cm length of glass tubing.

B. Fire Polishing. Fire polish the cut ends of the glass to make them smooth and safe to handle. Rotate one end of the glass tube or rod in the hottest part of the burner flame until the sharp edges have softened and become rounded (Fig. 1.7). Do

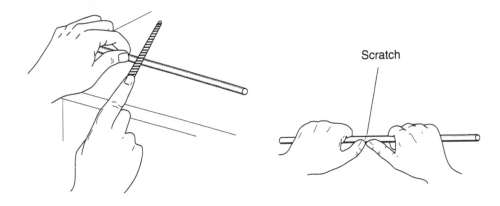

Scratch

Figure 1.6 Cutting glass tubing and rod.

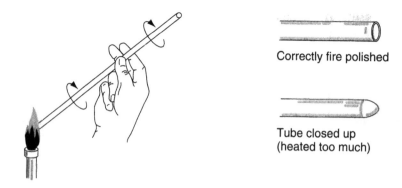

Correctly fire polished

*Tube closed up
(heated too much)*

Figure 1.7 *Fire polishing the cut end of a piece of glass.*

not hold the tubing in the flame too long. If you do, the hole in the tube will close. Place the hot glass on a wire gauze square to cool. ***Caution:*** *Hot glass and cold glass look alike; make sure one end of a piece of glass has cooled before you attempt to fire polish the other end!* When the glass is cool, fire polish the other end.

C. Bending Glass.   To bend glass tubing properly, it is necessary to heat about a 5-cm section of the tube all at once. This wide heating zone is best obtained by putting a wing top or flame spreader on your burner. Adjust the flame until it is blue and even across the top of the flame spreader. Grasp a 20-cm length of fire-polished glass tubing at both ends, and hold the center of it lengthwise in the flame just above the light blue inner portion—the hottest part of the flame. Rotate the tube in the flame to heat it uniformly until it becomes soft and just begins to sag (Fig. 1.8).

Remove the tube from the flame and bend it to the desired shape in one movement. When it has hardened, put it on a wire gauze square to cool. For practice, make two good right angle (90-degree) bends.

Show the articles you have made to your instructor.

Material Disposal   Your instructor will tell you how to dispose of the materials.

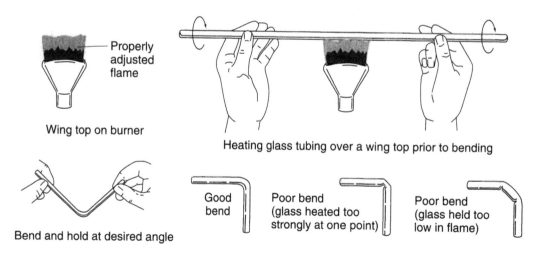

Properly
adjusted
flame

Wing top on burner

Heating glass tubing over a wing top prior to bending

Bend and hold at desired angle

Good
bend

Poor bend
(glass heated too
strongly at one point)

Poor bend
(glass held too
low in flame)

Figure 1.8 *Bending glass tubing.*

Experiment 1.4 Handling Liquids and Solids

Hypothesis   There is a correct way to dispense liquids and solids.

Objective   To learn the correct way to transfer liquids and solids.

SAFETY PRECAUTION	• **Wear safety goggles at all times while in the laboratory.**

Materials and Equipment   Wide-mouthed reagent bottles containing free-running table salt and caked table salt, 250-mL beakers, glass rod, spatula, dropper pipet, reagent bottle containing tap water, and watch glass

Procedure   **A. Transferring Liquids.**   Small volumes of a liquid are easily transferred with a dropper pipet. A large volume of a liquid is transferred from one container to another by directing its flow with a stirring rod, as shown in Figure 1.9.

Practice transferring a liquid from one container to another until you have mastered the technique. Figure 1.9 shows how the stopper from the reagent bottle is held between the fingers.

B. Transferring Solids.   Solid chemicals are usually stored in wide-mouthed screw-cap bottles. If the solid chemical flows freely, it can be poured or scooped out of the bottle. The correct procedures are illustrated in Figure 1.10. If the material has caked and does not flow readily, it must be loosened by shaking or broken into smaller pieces with a spatula so that it can be scooped out.

Practice transferring table salt (both the free-running and caked kinds) from its container to a watch glass and beaker. When the bottle cap is removed from the container, place it on the bench so that it cannot become contaminated. When you are finished with a chemical, replace the cap on the original container. **Caution:** *Do not return any unused reagent to its original container.*

Material Disposal   Your instructor will tell you how to dispose of the materials.

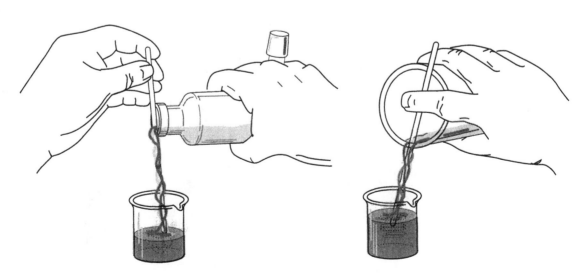

Figure 1.9 Controlling the transfer of a liquid.

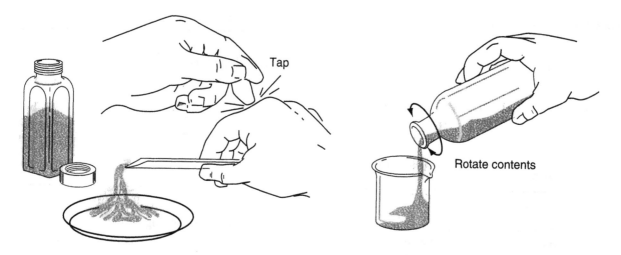

Tap

Rotate contents

Figure 1.10 *Transferring solid chemicals.*

Experiment 1.5 Filtration

Hypothesis   Particles suspended in a liquid do not pass through the pores in filter paper.

Objective   To separate insoluble particles from a liquid by filtration.

SAFETY PRECAUTION	• **Wear safety goggles at all times while in the laboratory.**

Materials and Equipment   Blackboard chalk, filter papers, ring stand, ring support, filter funnel, Buchner funnel, filter flask, glass rod, mortar and pestle, 100-mL beaker, 250-mL beaker, water aspirator or vacuum line, and washbottle filled with tap water

Procedure   Filtration is the separation of an insoluble solid from a liquid by pouring the mixture onto a barrier that allows the liquid but not the solid to pass through. The barrier is usually paper. The rate of liquid flow through the filter paper is assisted by gravity or vacuum.

A. Gravity Filtration.   Prepare a filter paper circle for gravity filtration by folding it in half and then in quarters. Now open the paper to form a cone with one thickness of paper on one side and three thicknesses on the other (Fig. 1.11).

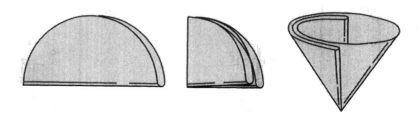

Figure 1.11 *Folding filter paper for gravity filtration.*

Put the paper cone in a filter funnel, and place the funnel in a ring on a ring stand. Moisten the filter paper with a small volume of water, and gently press the paper against the sides of the funnel to give a snug fit. If the correct size of filter paper is used, the top edge of the cone will be just below the rim of the filter funnel. Figure 1.12 shows the filtration apparatus. Notice that the tip of the filter funnel touches the inside surface of the collecting beaker and extends about an inch below the rim. Pour the mixture to be filtered down a glass rod into the funnel; take care to stay below the top edge of the filter paper. The filtered liquid or filtrate is collected in the beaker, while the solid particles are retained in the filter paper cone.

Grind a small piece of chalk, about 1 cm long, to a fine powder using a pestle and mortar. Transfer the powdered chalk to a 250-mL beaker, and add about 75 mL of water. Stir the mixture with a glass rod to make a suspension. Separate the chalk from the water by gravity filtration of 25 mL of the suspension. Carefully remove the filter paper and its contents from the filter funnel. Open the filter paper and allow the chalk to dry in the air.

B. Vacuum Filtration.   Vacuum filtration is done using a Buchner funnel and filter flask. The funnel is fitted into the flask by means of a one-holed rubber stopper or a rubber sleeve of appropriate size. The side arm of the filter flask is attached to a water aspirator or vacuum line with a short length of thick-walled rubber tubing as in Figure 1.13.

Place a piece of filter paper of the correct size on the Buchner funnel, turn the aspirator on, close the pinch clamp on the trap, and wet the filter paper with water. The filter paper should become securely fixed to the perforated base of the funnel. Using the same technique as in gravity filtration, transfer about 20 mL of the chalk suspension prepared in part A to the Buchner funnel. Continue to pull air through the chalk for a few minutes to dry it. When filtration is complete, the pinch clamp on the trap should be opened before the aspirator is turned off to avoid drawing water into the trap.

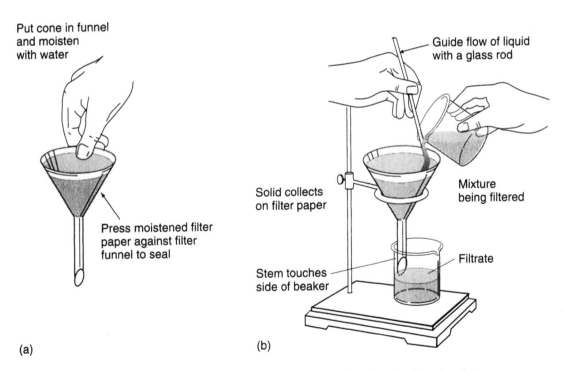

(a)   (b)

Figure 1.12 *Fitting the filter paper in the filter funnel (a) and the assembly of gravity filtration (b).*

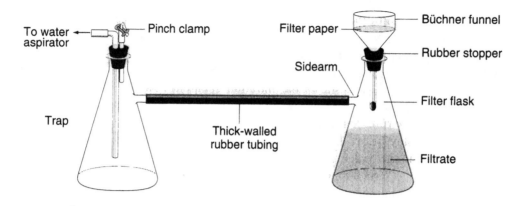

Figure 1.13 Vacuum filtration.

Material Disposal   Your instructor will tell you how to dispose of the materials.

Experiment 1

Prelaboratory Exercise

1. Why is it essential that you know and practice the laboratory safety rules?

2. Name two frequent causes of accidents in the chemistry laboratory.

3. Do you think contact lenses alone provide adequate eye protection in the chemistry laboratory? Explain.

4. Outline the procedure you would follow if your clothing were in flames.

5. What is the correct procedure for diluting concentrated acids?

6. Describe what you must do at the end of the laboratory period before leaving the laboratory.

7. How would you respond if your laboratory partner received a chemical splash in the eye?

Experiment 1.1   The Laboratory Gas Burner
Laboratory Report

1. Describe the burner flame when the air vents are closed.

2. When you hold an evaporating dish in the upper part of a luminous flame, what do you observe? Suggest a reason for your observation.

3. Where is the hottest region of the nonluminous flame?

4. What do you observe when the end of the copper wire is held in the hottest part of the burner flame for about 30 seconds?

5. Why doesn't the match head ignite when it is inside the blue inner cone?

6. What can happen to the flame if the gas flow is too great or too much air enters the air vents?

Postlaboratory Exercises

1. The type of laboratory burner used was _____ .

2. Describe what happens to the burner flame as the gas flow is reduced.

3. Describe what happens to the flame as the air vents are slowly changed from an open to the closed position.

4. Sketch a nonluminous flame, and label the hottest region of the flame.

5. Why do laboratory burners have adjustable air vents?

6. What may cause the flame to burn inside the barrel of the burner?

7. Give two reasons why the luminous flame is less desirable than the nonluminous flame as a source of heat in a laboratory experiment.

8. What causes a burner flame (a) to be smoky and (b) to separate from the tip of the burner?

9. What must you do if a burner strikes back?

Experiment 1.2 Heating Methods
Laboratory Report

1. List the safety precautions you must take when heating a liquid in a test tube.

2. Why must a beaker containing a liquid be placed on a wire gauze above a burner flame and not directly over the flame?

3. Explain why you must never boil a liquid in a plastic beaker above a burner flame.

Postlaboratory Exercises

1. If the flame intensity is left unchanged, what would happen if you lowered the beaker to just above the burner tube?

2. Why must you heat the liquid in a test tube a short distance below the surface of the liquid rather than at the bottom?

Experiment 1.3 Glassworking
Laboratory Report

1. List the safety precautions you must take when working with glass.

2. Why is it important to fire polish the cut ends of glass rod or tubing?

3. Instructor's comments on your glassworking projects.

Article	Comments
Glass rod/tube cut and fire polished	_____
	_____
Right-angle bends	_____
	_____

Postlaboratory Exercises

1. How do you cut a piece of glass tubing into two pieces?

2. How is the cut end of a piece of glass tubing fire polished?

3. Why is it important to fire polish the ends of glass tubing?

Experiment 1.4 Handling Liquids and Solids
Laboratory Report

1. How would you transfer a small volume of liquid?

2. When pouring a liquid from a reagent bottle, why do you hold the stopper from the bottle between your fingers?

3. Describe a convenient way to transfer a very small amount of a solid chemical from a reagent bottle to a reaction vessel.

Postlaboratory Exercises

1. How can a liquid be transferred from a bottle to a beaker without splashing and without running down the outside wall of the bottle?

2. What is the most convenient way to transfer a very small volume of liquid?

3. Suppose you had a free-running solid such as that used in this experiment. What do you think would be the easiest way to transfer this solid from the large-mouthed container to a small-mouthed one?

4. Why do you rotate a container of free-running solid while transferring the solid?

5. What is the purpose of tapping the back of the hand in one of the procedures?

Experiment 1.5   Filtration
Laboratory Report

1. Explain the term *suspension*. What is the composition of the suspension in this experiment?

2. Why must the end of the filter funnel touch the inside wall of the collecting beaker in gravity filtration?

3. Explain the term *filtrate*. What is the composition of the filtrate in this experiment?

4. If the filtrate in your experiment is not as clear as tap water, offer a possible explanation.

Postlaboratory Exercises

1. Which of the two filtration methods is more efficient? Explain the reasons for your choice.

2. Does gravity filtration have any advantages over vacuum-assisted filtration? What are they?

Length and Area

Taking measurements is important in everyday life. Common measurements include taking our temperature if we feel ill, checking tire pressures before leaving on an auto trip, and measuring ingredients when baking a cake. Taking measurements is also the basis for recording experimental results. Since chemistry is an experimental science, taking measurements is fundamental to chemists. In the United States, both the metric, or SI, system and the English system of measurement are widely used, but for scientific purposes, the metric system is used exclusively. In this laboratory exercise you will use the metric units of length and volume and will determine the relationship between the metric and the English units of length. The importance of taking measurements properly and of knowing the significance of your measurements will be emphasized.

Significant Figures. When scientists report measurements, they use significant figures. The significant figures in a measurement include all the digits that are known accurately plus a last digit that is estimated. For example, when length is measured using a foot rule calibrated in intervals of one-tenth inch, it is possible to report a length to the nearest tenth of an inch, but it is also possible to estimate the length to the nearest hundredth of an inch. Suppose we estimate a length that lies between 3.7 in. and 3.8 in. to be 3.76 in. This number has three significant figures. The first two digits (3 and 7) are known with certainty, but the last digit (6) is an estimate and has some uncertainty. Scientists can obtain some additional information by estimating the last digit in a measurement. The digits retained in a measurement are all significant figures, although the last digit is uncertain. If we have a measuring device that is calibrated in 0.01-in. intervals and some means of magnifying the scale, we can report a length to the nearest 0.001 in. We might report the length as 3.762 in. This measurement has four significant figures, and the last digit (2) is uncertain.

Every nonzero digit in a recorded measurement is significant. The numbers 12.6 and 391 each have three significant figures. Zeros appearing between nonzero digits are significant. Zeros at the end of a number may be significant. Zeros appearing in front of all the nonzero digits are never significant. Let us look at some examples:

Number	Significant figures
104	3
45.02	4
0.72	2
0.00302	3
2.0620	5

Zeros to the right of the last nonzero digit but to the left of the decimal point, as in the numbers 500, 2000, and 37,500, may be significant, or they may just serve as place markers to show the size of the number. One way to avoid confusion is to write all numbers in scientific notation. For example, if a length of 300 in. is known to two significant figures, it would be written 3.0×10^2 in. If the length is known to three significant figures, we write 3.00×10^2 in.

The result of an addition or subtraction can have no more digits to the right of the decimal point than there are in the measurement with the fewest digits to the right of the decimal point. If the digit immediately following the last digit that we may keep is less than 5, all the digits after the last significant place are dropped. If the digit immediately following the last digit we may keep is 5 or greater, the value of the digit in the last significant place is increased by 1. Here are two examples:

(a)   4.63
      15.18
      273.4
      293.21

The answer must be rounded off to one digit after the decimal point.

Answer = 293.2

(b)   52.686
      −13.73
      38.956

The answer must be rounded off to two digits after the decimal point.

Answer = 38.96

In calculations involving multiplication or division, the answer must contain no more significant figures than the measurement in the problem with the fewest significant figures. In multiplication and division, the position of the decimal point has nothing to do with the number of significant figures. Examine the following examples:

(a) $3.26 \times 0.56 = 1.8256$
$= 1.8$ (because 0.56 has two significant figures)

(b) $7.38 \times 0.0008264 = 0.00609883$
$= 6.09883 \times 10^{-3}$
$= 6.10 \times 10^{-3}$ (because 7.38 has three significant figures)

(c) $43.618 \div 3.7 = 11.7886$
$= 12$ (because 3.7 has two significant figures)

(d) $5.37 \div 0.3235 = 16.5996$
$= 16.6$ (because 5.37 has three significant figures)

Accuracy and Precision.   To scientists, the words *accuracy* and *precision* mean different things. In measurements, accuracy is concerned with how close a measurement comes to the actual dimension or true value of whatever is measured. Precision is concerned with how close together a series of measurements of the same quantity are. It is a measure of the reproducibility of the measurement.

Suppose, for example, a length of exactly 20.00 cm is measured five times, and the recorded values to four significant figures are

$$20.03 \text{ cm}$$
$$20.02 \text{ cm}$$
$$19.90 \text{ cm}$$
$$20.01 \text{ cm}$$
$$19.94 \text{ cm}$$

These results are both accurate and precise; each measurement is close to the true value of exactly 20.00 cm, and the measurements have good reproducibility, since they agree very closely with one another.

An experimenter does not usually report all measurements but calculates a mean or average value. The mean is obtained by dividing the sum of the measured values by the number of measurements made:

$$20.03 \text{ cm}$$
$$20.02 \text{ cm}$$
$$19.90 \text{ cm}$$
$$20.01 \text{ cm}$$
$$\underline{19.94 \text{ cm}}$$

$$\text{Sum} = 99.90 \text{ cm}$$

$$\text{Mean} = \frac{99.90 \text{ cm}}{5} = 19.98 \text{ cm}$$

Since each value is accurate, the mean value is accurate and precise.

Is a precise measurement always accurate? Not necessarily. Suppose you measure the same 20.00-cm length using a rule with the first 3 cm sawed off, but you neglect to take this into account. You may report

$$23.03 \text{ cm}$$
$$23.02 \text{ cm}$$
$$22.90 \text{ cm}$$
$$23.01 \text{ cm}$$
$$\underline{22.94 \text{ cm}}$$
$$\text{Sum} = 114.90 \text{ cm}$$

$$\text{Mean} = \frac{114.90 \text{ cm}}{5} = 22.98 \text{ cm}$$

These results are precise, but neither the individual measurements nor the mean is accurate. You would report a length of exactly 20.00 cm as 22.98 cm!

As a third example, consider a similar set of results obtained by a careless worker:

$$21.8 \text{ cm}$$
$$18.3 \text{ cm}$$
$$19.2 \text{ cm}$$
$$20.9 \text{ cm}$$
$$\underline{20.3 \text{ cm}}$$

$$\text{Sum} = 100.5 \text{ cm}$$

$$\text{Mean} = \frac{100.5 \text{ cm}}{5} = 20.1 \text{ cm}$$

Obviously, the individual results lack accuracy, and the group of measurements is not very precise. The accuracy of real measurements often depends on the quality of the measuring device, whereas precision often depends on the skill of the person making the measurements. Usually we must assume that the measuring devices we use in the laboratory are as accurate as their manufacturers specify. Our job is to use these devices with enough care to obtain good precision.

Hypothesis

In doing experiments, it is important to take measurements properly and to report results to the correct number of significant figures.

Objectives

1. To recognize the number of significant figures in a measurement.
2. To measure lengths in the metric system using a meter rule.
3. To calculate areas in the metric system.
4. To measure lengths in inches and to determine the factor for converting inches to centimeters.

SAFETY PRECAUTION	· **Wear safety goggles at all times while in the laboratory.**

Materials and Equipment

Meter stick and foot rule graduated in tenths of an inch

Procedure

Examine a meter stick and a foot rule. Measure the length and width of this book page both in centimeters and in inches, and record your results on the laboratory report. State the number of significant figures in each measurement. Do the calculations, and report your answers to the correct number of significant figures.

Material Disposal

Nothing for disposal.

Experiment 2

Prelaboratory Exercises

1. The base unit of length in the metric system is _____ .

2. How many centimeters are in a meter?

3. How many millimeters are in a centimeter?

4. A rectangular piece of paper measures 2.5 cm by 8.5 cm. What is the area of the paper? (Don't forget the units.)

5.

Round off this number	To this number of significant figures	Answer
4.0361	4	_____
7.482	1	_____
0.00272	2	_____
7.193×10^4	3	_____
2.3052×10^{-3}	3	_____

Experiment 2
Laboratory Report

Page length: _____ cm   Number of significant figures: _____

_____ in.   Number of significant figures: _____

Page width: _____ cm   Number of significant figures: _____

_____ in.   Number of significant figures: _____

Area of page (length × width)

_____ cm × _____ cm = _____ cm^2 = _____ cm^2 (rounded off to the correct number of significant figures)

_____ in. × _____ in. = _____ in.^{2} = _____ in.^{2} (rounded off to the correct number of significant figures)

Conversion factor: inches to centimeters

$$\frac{\text{Page length (cm)}}{\text{Page length (in.)}} = \frac{\text{_____ cm}}{\text{_____ in.}} = \text{_____ cm/in.}$$

$$\frac{\text{Page width (cm)}}{\text{Page width (in.)}} = \frac{\text{_____ cm}}{\text{_____ in.}} = \text{_____ cm/in.}$$

Conversion factor from textbook: _____ cm/in.

Postlaboratory Exercises

1. Convert the following quantities to meters.
- (a) 50 cm
- (b) 3.5×10^4 cm
- (c) 0.02 cm

2. Convert the following quantities to millimeters.
- (a) 8.2×10^{-3} m
- (b) 16 cm
- (c) 0.025 cm

3. Convert the following quantities to centimeters.
- (a) 4.5 in.
- (b) 0.6 in.
- (c) 2.6×10^{-3} m

4. A rectangular sheet of paper measures 8.5 in. by 11 in. Calculate the area of this paper in (a) square inches and (b) square centimeters.

(a) —————— in.^{2}

(b) —————— cm^2

Volume

The unit for measuring volume in the metric system is the liter (L). The volumes used in laboratory experiments are generally smaller than a liter. They are measured in milliliters (mL). A milliliter is one-thousandth part of a liter, so

$$1000 \text{ mL} = 1 \text{ L} \qquad \text{or} \qquad 1 \text{ mL} = 10^{-3} \text{ L}$$

The cubic centimeter (cm^3) is equal to the milliliter:

$$1 \text{ mL} = 1 \text{ cm}^3$$

Volume measurements are important in many experimental procedures. Sometimes volume measurements must be accurate, but at other times they can be approximate. Most volume measures in the laboratory are made using equipment calibrated in milliliters. Although some beakers have graduation marks, these marks are designed only for quick, rough estimates of volume. Accurate volumes must be measured with pipets, burets, or volumetric flasks (Fig. 3.1).

Hypothesis A variety of methods can be used to make accurate volume measurements.

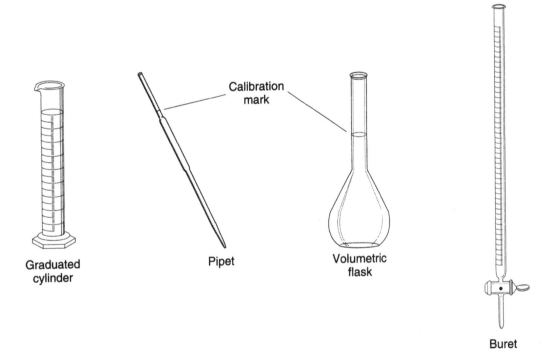

Graduated cylinder

Pipet

Calibration mark

Volumetric flask

Buret

Figure 3.1 Examples of volumetric glassware.

Figure 3.2 *The meniscus.*

Objectives

1. To make volume measurements in the metric system using a graduated beaker, graduated cylinder, pipet, buret, and volumetric flask.
2. To calculate volumes in the metric system.
3. To measure the volume of small, irregularly shaped solid objects.

SAFETY PRECAUTION

• **Wear safety goggles at all times while in the laboratory.**

Materials and Equipment

Small pebbles, pieces of metal, 250-mL graduated beaker, 25-mL and 100-mL graduated cylinders, 10-mL graduated pipet, 25-mL volumetric pipet, 50-mL buret, 100-mL volumetric flask, small test tube, calipers, 250-mL Erlenmeyer flask, pipet bulb, paper towels, and tap water

Procedure

A. Making a Volume Measurement. Half-fill a 100-mL graduated cylinder with water, and set the cylinder on your laboratory bench. Examine the surface of the water. Notice how the surface curves upward where the water contacts the cylinder walls. This curved surface is called a *meniscus* (Fig. 3.2).

A volume measurement is always read at the bottom of the meniscus with your eye at the same level as the liquid surface. To make the meniscus more visible, you can place your finger or a dark piece of paper behind and just below the meniscus while making the reading (Fig. 3.3).

Graduated cylinders are available in many capacities. The 100-mL cylinder is marked in 1-mL divisions, and volumes can be estimated to the nearest 0.1 mL. The

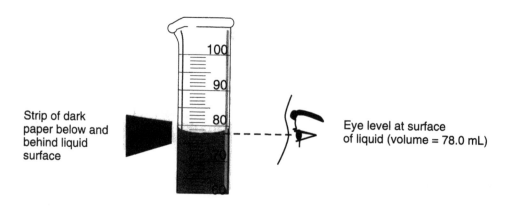

Figure 3.3 *Reading the volume in a graduated cylinder.*

last digit in these measurements is therefore significant but uncertain. Record the volume of water in your graduated cylinder in the laboratory report.

B. Measuring the Volume of a Small, Irregularly Shaped Object by Displacement. Select several small solid objects that will fit into your graduated cylinder. Half-fill your graduated cylinder with water, and record the volume in the data table. This is your initial volume. (Do not waste time in an attempt to get an exact initial volume such as 10.0 mL or 20.0 mL. Experiments seldom give results that are nice easy numbers.) Tilt your graduated cylinder, and allow an object to slide slowly and without splashing into the water. The object must be completely immersed. Place the cylinder on a level surface, and measure the new volume. This is the final volume. The difference between the final and initial volumes is the volume of the object. If there is still room in the cylinder, determine the volume of another object. Record your results in the data table.

C. Measured Volume of a Test Tube. Fill a small test tube to the top with water. Pour the water into a clean, dry 100-mL graduated cylinder, and read and record the volume. Fill the test tube with water again, and add this to the water in the graduated cylinder. Read the new volume. Repeat the process three more times for a total of five operations. When all the volumes have been recorded in the data table, calculate an average volume for the test tube.

D. Calculated Volume of a Test Tube. Measure the length and inside diameter of the test tube used in part C, and record the measurements. Calculate the volume of the test tube assuming that it is a cylinder. (It is preferable to use calipers to make these measurements, particularly the inside diameter.) Compare the measured and calculated volumes for the test tube.

E. Using Pipets. A pipet is used to accurately measure and deliver volumes of liquids. Two types are commonly used in chemistry laboratories: volumetric pipets and measuring or graduated pipets (Fig. 3.4).

A volumetric pipet has a single calibration mark and delivers the volume printed on the bulb of the pipet at the temperature specified. The pipet in the figure delivers exactly 25 mL if used at 20 °C. A measuring or graduated pipet has calibrations along the length of the pipet and can deliver any desired volume within its measuring range. Volumes can be measured more accurately with a volumetric pipet than with a graduated pipet.

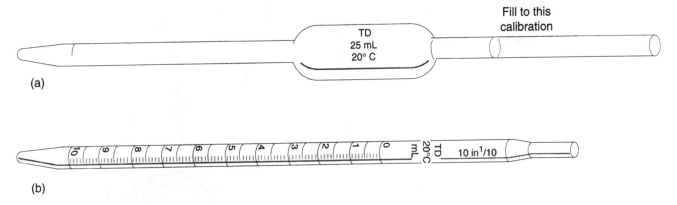

Figure 3.4 *The volumetric pipet (a) and the measuring or graduated pipet (b).*

Pipets are filled by suction. To transfer an exact volume of liquid from a beaker to an Erlenmeyer flask, place the pipet tip below the surface of the liquid, and press a compressed pipet bulb against the upper end of the pipet (Fig. 3.5). **Caution:** *Never fill a pipet by applying suction with your mouth.* Slowly release pressure on the bulb so that liquid is drawn into the pipet to a level about 2 cm above the desired volume mark. Remove the bulb, and quickly place your index finger over the end of the pipet. Withdraw the pipet from the liquid, and wipe the outside of the stem with a paper towel. Carefully reduce the pressure on your finger to allow the excess liquid to drain into the beaker until the bottom of the meniscus is at the desired calibration mark. When releasing liquid from a measuring pipet, touch the tip of the pipet to the inside wall of the flask, and allow the liquid to drain to the correct point. When releasing liquid from a volumetric pipet, let it drain completely, wait about 20 seconds, and then touch the pipet tip to the side of the flask to remove some of the liquid in the tip. The pipet delivers the stated volume when this procedure is used even though a small amount of liquid remains in the tip. Do *not* blow out a measuring pipet or a volumetric pipet. Figure 3.5 shows the procedure for filling and emptying a volumetric pipet.

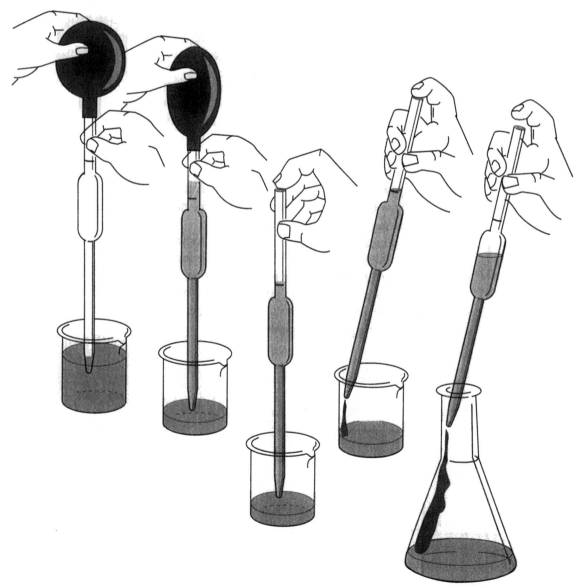

Figure 3.5 *Filling and emptying a pipet.*

Practice filling a 25-mL volumetric pipet and a 10-mL graduated pipet with water using the procedure outlined above until you have mastered the technique. Now, to test your skill, transfer four 25-mL portions of distilled water with a volumetric pipet to a clean, dry 100-mL volumetric flask. How near is the final volume of water to the graduation mark on the flask? Record your comment in the laboratory report.

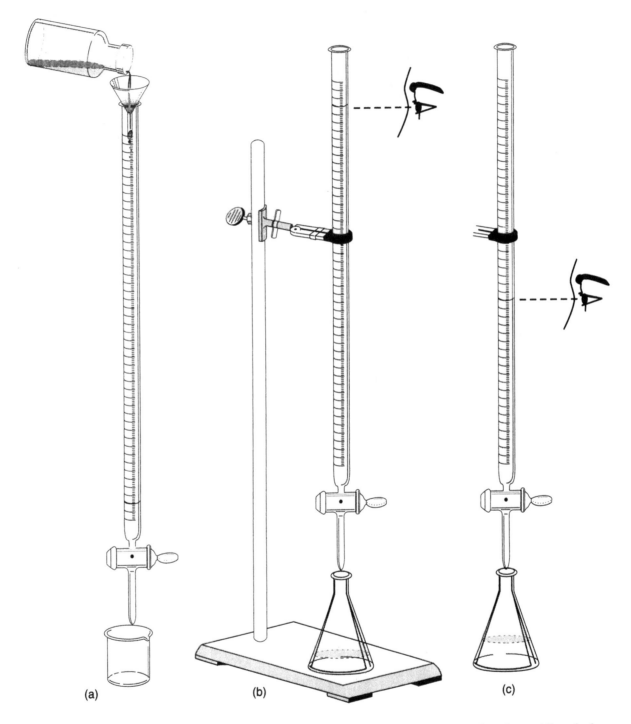

(a) (b) (c)

Figure 3.6 *Filling and emptying a buret. (a) Use a few milliliters of the solution to rinse a clean buret. Allow the buret to drain. (b) Fill the buret above the zero mark. Open the stopcock briefly to remove the air from the tip. Record the initial reading. (c) Slowly run the solution into the receiving vessel. At the end of the titration turn the stopcock off, and allow the buret to drain 20 seconds. Record the final reading.*

F. Using a Buret.   A buret is designed to deliver a precisely measured volume of liquid. It consists of a narrow graduated tube equipped with a tap, or stopcock, for controlling the flow of liquid.

The 25-mL buret and 50-mL buret are commonly used in the chemistry laboratory. Both have calibrations divided into 0.1-mL intervals so volumes can be estimated to 0.01 mL. It is important to make sure the liquid in a buret is free of air bubbles and that the tip of the buret is full of liquid. When delivering the liquid, the stopcock is usually turned with the left hand, and the receiving vessel is held in the right hand. Your instructor will demonstrate the technique for filling, reading, and dispensing liquid from a buret (Fig. 3.6). You should not adjust the initial level of the liquid in the buret to exactly 0.00 mL. Any volume on the scale will do as long as you record it accurately.

Practice dispensing liquid from a buret. Fill a clean, dry 25-mL graduated cylinder exactly to the 20-mL mark with water delivered from your buret. Record your results in the data table.

Material Disposal   Your instructor will tell you how to dispose of the materials.

Experiment 3

Prelaboratory Exercises

1. The base unit of volume in the metric system is the _____ .

2. A box measures 6.0 cm × 5.0 cm × 4.0 cm. What is the volume of the box? (Don't forget units.)

3. What is the volume of the box in liters?

4. What is the formula for the volume of a cylinder?

5. A can of oil has a diameter of 8.0 cm and a height of 10.0 cm. What is the volume of the can?

Experiment 3
Laboratory Report

A. Volume of water in the 100-mL graduated cylinder: _____

B. Volume of irregularly shaped object by displacement: _____

Object	Initial volume	Final volume	Volume of object
(a) _____	_____	_____	_____
(b) _____	_____	_____	_____

C. Measured volume of test tube: _____
Volume of water in the graduated cylinder after

First addition   = _____ mL

Second addition = _____ mL

Third addition   = _____ mL

Fourth addition = _____ mL

Fifth addition   = _____ mL = final volume

$$\text{Average volume} = \frac{\text{final volume}}{5} = \frac{\quad\quad}{5} \text{ mL} = \text{_____ mL}$$

D. Calculated volume of test tube: _____

Length: _____ cm

Inside diameter: _____ cm

$$\text{Radius} = \frac{\text{diameter}}{2} = \text{_____ cm}$$

Volume of test tube = $\pi \times (\text{radius})^2 \times (\text{length})$

$$= 3.14 \times (\text{_____ cm})^2 \times (\text{_____ cm})$$

$$= \text{_____ cm}^3$$

Compare the measured volume from part C to the calculated volume from part D, and make a comment.

E. Filling a 100-mL volumetric flask with water from a 25-mL pipet.

Observation: _____

_____

_____

F. Filling a graduated cylinder with water from a buret.

Initial buret reading: _____

Final buret reading: _____

Measured volume of 20 mL in cylinder: _____

Postlaboratory Exercises

1. How many milliliters is 2.57×10^{-3} L?

2. Given the volumes 25.76 mL, 25.32 mL, and 25.51 mL, calculate the average volume:

Average volume = _____

3. What are the two types of pipets used in the laboratory? Which is more accurate?

4. What is the purpose of wiping the pipet stem between transfers?

Mass

Mass is the quantity of matter an object contains. The SI unit of mass is the kilogram (kg); the derived unit of mass most commonly used in the laboratory is the gram (g). In the laboratory, measurements of mass are made with a balance. The accurate determination of mass is a fundamental technique that must be mastered by all students of chemistry.

Many kinds of balances are seen in chemistry laboratories. The most common types of balances found in introductory chemistry laboratories are the triple-beam or centigram balance, the top-loading balance, and the digital electronic balance (Fig. 4.1). The capacities and sensitivities (limits of detection) of these balances are given in the following table:

Type of balance	Maximum capacity (typical)	Sensitivity (limit of detection)
Centigram	300 g	0.01 g
Top-loading	160 g	0.001 g
Digital electronic	200 g	0.01 g–0.001 g

The following general rules apply to the use of all laboratory balances.

1. Check the balance before you start measuring mass. The balance pan should be empty and clean, and all dials or controls should be set on zero. The balance must be level; check the bubble level on the base. See your instructor if you need assistance with checking your balance.

2. Objects to be placed directly on the balance pan must be clean, dry, and at room temperature. Solid chemicals and liquids must never be put directly on the balance pan. Liquid samples should be contained in beakers or sealed containers. Solid chemicals can be conveniently put into beakers or disposable plastic weighing boats.

3. The balance is a precision instrument that must be handled with care. If applicable, always be sure that the balance is in an arrested position when objects are placed on or removed from the pan. Always turn all balance controls slowly.

4. Never move or jar either a balance or the balance table.

5. If you spill a chemical on or near the balance, clean it up immediately, and inform your laboratory instructor. A camel-hair brush is available to wipe minute traces of solid from the balance pan before you use it.

6. Never attempt to measure the mass of an object with a mass greater than the maximum capacity of the balance.

7. When you finish, return all balance controls to zero, and make sure the balance pan is clean.

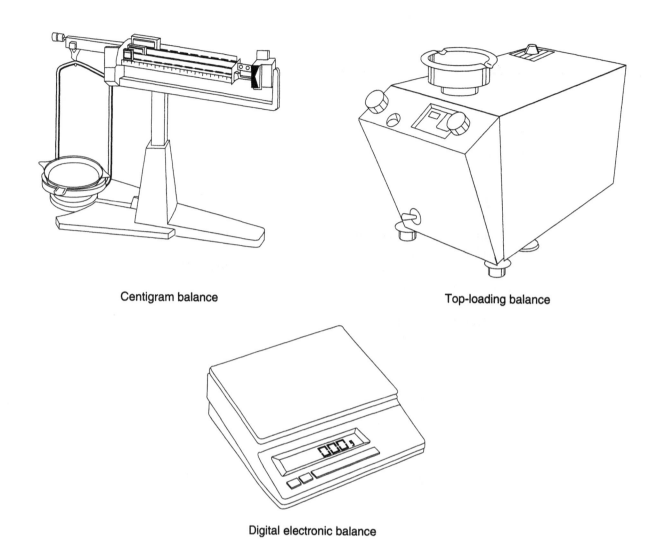

Centigram balance

Top-loading balance

Digital electronic balance

Figure 4.1 *Laboratory balances.*

Hypothesis

The mass of an object can be found by comparing it with a known mass.

Objectives

1. To learn to use a laboratory balance.
2. To determine the mass of an object by (a) measuring its mass directly and (b) measuring its mass by difference.

SAFETY PRECAUTION

- **Wear safety goggles at all times while in the laboratory.**

Materials and Equipment

Small pieces of metal, rubber stoppers, 100-mL beaker, and laboratory balance

Procedure

Your laboratory instructor will describe and demonstrate the operation of the balances in your laboratory. As you do this experiment, recall the general rules that were given in the introductory section.

A. Measuring Mass Directly. Measure the mass of several solid objects directly on the balance pan, and record the masses as accurately as possible in the data table. Some objects will be provided in the laboratory, but you may use other items such as coins, keys, or small beakers.

B. Measuring Mass by Difference. Most mass measurements in the chemistry laboratory are done by difference. Place a container such as a beaker on the balance pan, and measure its mass. Place the object whose mass you want to know (e.g., a rubber stopper) in the container, and then determine the combined mass. Finally, obtain the mass of the object by subtracting the mass of the container from the mass of the container and the object.

Determine the mass of the same object by direct determination. Enter your results on the report sheet.

For more practice, determine the masses of three small objects separately, and take the sum of the masses. Compare this total mass with one obtained by measuring the mass of all three objects together.

Material Disposal   Your instructor will tell you how to dispose of the materials.

Experiment 4

Prelaboratory Exercises

1. What is mass, and how is it measured in the chemistry laboratory?

2. Name the unit of mass most commonly used in the chemistry laboratory. Is it an SI unit?

3. What is weight?

Experiment 4
Laboratory Report

Type and name of balance used: _____

Balance sensitivity: _____   Maximum capacity: _____

A. Measuring Mass Directly

Object	Mass measurement
(a) _____	_____
(b) _____	_____
(c) _____	_____
(d) _____	_____

B. Measuring Mass by Difference

Mass of empty beaker: _____

Mass of beaker and stopper: _____

Mass of stopper (by difference):   _____

Mass of stopper (direct):   _____

Mass difference between the two methods: _____

More practice:

Object	Mass
(a) _____	_____
(b) _____	_____
(c) _____	_____

Total mass = _____

Direct mass determination
of all three objects together = _____

Comment on how the two values compare:

Postlaboratory Exercises

1. Why must you never put chemicals directly on the balance pan?

2. You measure the mass of an empty beaker on a balance and use a different balance to measure the mass of the same beaker after you have put some sodium chloride into it. You then report the mass of sodium chloride by difference. Comment on this procedure.

3. Which is the preferred method, measuring the mass of an object directly or by difference? Give reasons for your choice.

4. Why must an object be at room temperature when you measure its mass on a balance?

Density and Specific Gravity

Density is an easily measured physical property that is very useful for the identification of unknown materials. Substances that have similar physical appearances often have quite different densities. In this experiment you will determine the densities of some common solids and liquids.

Density is the ratio of the mass of an object to its volume:

$$\text{Density} = \frac{\text{mass}}{\text{volume}}$$

Density has units of grams per cubic centimeter (g/cm^3) when mass is measured in grams and volume in cubic centimeters. Since $1\ cm^3$ is the same volume as $1\ mL$, densities are frequently reported in grams per milliliter (g/mL). The densities of some common substances are as follows:

Substance	Density at 25 °C, g/cm^3
Lead	11.3
Silver	10.5
Iron	7.86
Aluminum	2.70
Concrete	2.3
Water	1.00
Ethanol	0.83
Gasoline	0.75

Specific gravity is a comparison of the density of a substance to the density of a reference substance, usually at the same temperature. Water at 4 °C, which has a density of $1\ g/cm^3$, is commonly used as the reference for this measurement unless otherwise specified.

$$\text{Specific gravity} = \frac{\text{density of substance, } g/cm^3}{\text{density of water, } g/cm^3}$$

The units cancel; therefore, specific gravity is a unitless number.

To determine the density of a solid object, both its mass and its volume must first be determined. The mass can be obtained by direct weighing or weighing by difference. The volume can be obtained either by displacement of water in a graduated cylinder, provided the substance to be measured is insoluble, or by calculation from its dimensions if it is a regular shape such as a cube, sphere, or cylinder (see Experiment 3, part B, on page 33).

Figure 5.1 *Hydrometer.*

The specific gravity of a liquid can be measured with a hydrometer (Fig. 5.1). The calibration mark on the hydrometer stem at the surface of the liquid indicates the specific gravity of the liquid. A hydrometer used to determine the specific gravity of urine is called a *urinometer*. The specific gravity of urine can be valuable in medical diagnoses. Normal urine has a specific gravity in the range of 1.010 to 1.030. A specific gravity below 1.010 may indicate diabetes insipidus or kidney damage; a specific gravity above 1.030 may indicate diabetes mellitus or congestive heart failure.

Hypothesis

Density is a characteristic or intensive property of matter.

Objectives

1. To calculate the density of a solid by measuring its mass and volume.
2. To determine the density of a liquid.
3. To use a hydrometer to measure the specific gravity of a liquid.

| **SAFETY PRECAUTIONS** | • **Wear safety goggles at all times while in the laboratory.**
• **Isopropyl alcohol is flammable; keep it away from open flames.** |

Materials and Equipment

Isopropyl alcohol (2-propanol), 10% sodium chloride, small cylindrical pieces of metal, rubber stoppers, lead shot, 25-mL graduated cylinder, laboratory balance, hydrometer, thermometer, and 250-mL glass cylinder

Procedure

A. Density of a Solid. Determine the densities of a rubber stopper, a solid metal cylinder, and lead supplied as lead shot. The measurements you must make are identified on the report sheet. Remember to include units in measurements.

B. Density of a Liquid. Determine the density of water and of an unknown liquid. The measurements you need to make are indicated on the report sheet.

C. Specific Gravity. Use a hydrometer to measure the specific gravity of the liquids provided in the laboratory. Measure the temperature of the liquids. Record the results on the report sheet.

Material Disposal

Your instructor will tell you how to dispose of the materials.

Experiment 5

Prelaboratory Exercises

1. The ratio of the mass of an object to its volume is called _____ .

2. The units of density are _____ .

3. A block of metal weighs 27.0 g and has a volume of 10.0 mL. Calculate the density of the metal.

4. What is specific gravity? Cite a use of specific gravity measurements in hospitals.

Experiment 5
Laboratory Report

A. Density of a Solid

  (a) Rubber stopper

   Mass of rubber stopper (direct): _____

   Initial volume in graduated cylinder (water only): _____

   Final volume in graduated cylinder
   (water and stopper): _____

   Volume of rubber stopper (by difference): _____

   Density of rubber stopper (show calculations below): _____

  (b) Metal cylinder

   Mass of metal cylinder (direct): _____

   Length of cylinder: _____

   Diameter of cylinder: _____

   Volume of cylinder (calculated): _____

   Density of metal cylinder (show calculations below): _____

(c) Lead shot

Mass of beaker: _____

Mass of beaker and lead shot: _____

Mass of lead shot (should be about 50 g): _____

Initial volume in graduated cylinder (water only): _____

Final volume in graduated cylinder
(lead shot and water): _____

Volume of lead shot: _____

Density of lead shot (show calculations below): _____

B. Density of a Liquid

(a) Water

Mass of empty graduated cylinder: _____

Mass of graduated cylinder and 25.0 mL of water: _____

Mass of 25.0 mL of water: _____

Density of water (show calculations below): _____

(b) Unknown liquid

Mass of empty graduated cylinder: _____

Mass of graduated cylinder and 25.0 mL of unknown liquid: _____

Mass of 25.0 mL of unknown liquid: _____

Density of unknown liquid (show calculations below): _____

Name of unknown liquid: _____

Reported density: _____

C. Specific Gravity

Liquid	Specific gravity	Temperature
Water	_____	_____
10% Sodium chloride	_____	_____
Isopropyl alcohol	_____	_____

Postlaboratory Exercises

1. A solid metal object with a mass of 24.6 g is placed in a graduated cylinder containing 25.0 mL of water. The water level rises from 25.0 to 33.2 mL. Calculate the density of the metal.

2. What is the volume of a pure silver nugget that has a mass of 8.80 g?

3. Why is specific gravity a unitless number?

4. A solution has a specific gravity of 1.35. Calculate the mass of 25.0 mL of this solution.

Physical and Chemical Properties and Changes

A good understanding of material things requires an understanding of the physical and chemical characteristics of matter. A few planned experiments can help us hone our powers of observation and begin to learn how scientists view the world.

Physical and Chemical Properties. The physical properties of a substance can be observed and measured without changing the composition of the substance. Physical properties of matter include odor, color, density, solubility, boiling point and melting point, and its physical state at room temperature. Physical properties can be used to describe and identify substances. A colorless, odorless liquid that freezes at 0 °C and boils at 100 °C is probably water, for example. Every substance also has chemical properties. Chemical properties, however, are observed only when a substance undergoes a change in composition—a chemical reaction.

Physical and Chemical Changes. Matter can undergo many changes. Sometimes only the physical state, temperature, or particle size of matter changes. Ice melts and gasoline evaporates, for example. These changes are physical changes. When iron rusts or wood burns, new substances of different chemical composition than the starting substances are produced. Changes of this type are chemical reactions. Some chemical reactions can be observed because the products of the reaction have different physical properties than the reactants. The evolution of a gas, a color change, the formation of a precipitate, and the evolution of heat are frequently telltale signs that a chemical reaction is occurring.

You will examine some substances and describe their physical properties in this experiment. You will cause changes in some of these substances. You will decide whether the changes are physical or chemical using tests and making observations. You also will demonstrate that mass is conserved in physical and chemical changes.

Hypotheses

1. Physical changes are often easily reversed.
2. Chemical changes are often not easily reversed.

Objectives

1. To study some properties of matter.
2. To separate mixtures according to differences in physical properties of the components.
3. To induce changes in matter.
4. To classify changes as physical or chemical.
5. To show that mass is conserved in a physical or chemical change.

Materials and Equipment

Powdered sulfur, iron powder, sodium bicarbonate (baking soda), sodium chloride (table salt), sucrose (cane sugar), sand, magnesium ribbon, 6 *M* hydrochloric acid, magnet, laboratory balance, spatula, small test tubes, filter funnel, filter paper, 100-mL beaker, watch glass, evaporating dish, magnifying glass, crucible tongs, test tube rack, glass stirring rod, water bath (ring stand, ring clamp, wire gauze, burner, 250-mL beaker), and high-purity water

Procedure

A. The Physical Properties of Matter. Use clean spatulas to transfer to clean sheets of paper a sample about the size of a pea of each of the following substances: powdered sulfur, iron filings, sodium bicarbonate, sodium chloride, sucrose, and sand. Place two 5-cm pieces of magnesium ribbon on a paper. Write the name of each substance on its sheet of paper. Examine each substance carefully. Test the effect of a magnet on each substance by passing the magnet under the sample of the paper. (To avoid contamination, do not dip the magnet into the substances being tested.) Test the solubility of each substance in water by adding an amount of sample the size of a match head to about 3 mL of high-purity water in a test tube. Stopper the test tube, and shake it briefly. Record your observations on the report sheet.

B. Causing a Physical Change. Combine the remaining samples of iron filings and sulfur on one piece of paper, and mix them thoroughly with a spatula. Examine the mixture with a magnifying glass, and move a magnet under the paper holding the mixture. Record your observations. *(Keep this mixture for Experiment 6, part D.)*

Combine the salt and sand on one piece of paper, and mix thoroughly. Examine the mixture with a magnifying glass, and test the effect of a magnet. Record your observations.

Transfer the salt-sand mixture to a clean 100-mL beaker, add about 30 mL of water, and stir with a glass rod for about 1 minute. Filter the mixture by gravity (you may wish to review Experiment 1.5), and collect the filtrate in a 100-mL beaker. Pour about 10 mL of the filtrate into a clean evaporating dish. Place the evaporating dish on a beaker of boiling water (see Fig. 6.1) until the filtrate has evaporated to dryness. Remove the filter paper and its contents from the filter funnel. Examine the residue in the evaporating dish and the residue on the filter paper, and report your findings.

C. Causing a Chemical Change. Grasp one end of a strip of magnesium ribbon with your crucible tongs, and hold it in a burner flame until it ignites. *Caution: Do not look directly at the burning magnesium.* Allow the combustion product to fall onto a clean watch glass. Compare its appearance with that of the unburned strip of magnesium, and report your findings.

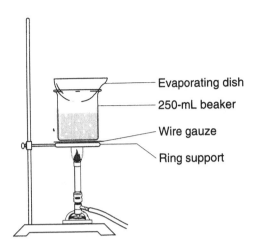

Evaporating dish
250-mL beaker
Wire gauze
Ring support

Figure 6.1 *Evaporation of water from the filtrate.*

Place the unburned strip of magnesium and the combustion product of the burned strip in separate, clean test tubes, and add 5 or 6 drops of 6 *M* hydrochloric acid to each. Record your observations.

Transfer half the sucrose sample to a clean dry test tube, and heat it gently in a burner flame. *Caution: Hold the test tube with a holder.* Periodically check the odor at the mouth of the test tube by wafting the fumes toward you, and note any change in the appearance of the sucrose. Look for a condensate on the upper end of the test tube.

Place the tube on a wire gauze to cool. Scrape some of the residue out of the tube. Examine the residue, and test its water solubility as described in Experiment 6, part A. As a comparison, test the water solubility of the original sample of sucrose.

Transfer the sodium bicarbonate sample to a clean dry test tube. Observe the system as you carefully add 5 drops of dilute hydrochloric acid to sodium bicarbonate. Touch the bottom of the test tube to the palm of your hand. Record your observations.

D. Conservation of Mass. Transfer approximately equal quantities of the iron filings and sulfur mixture you made earlier (Experiment 6, part B) to two clean, dry test tubes. Put one of the tubes in a test tube rack. Measure the mass of the other test tube and its contents accurately, and record the mass. *Caution: The heating must be done only in a fume hood, and the test tube must be held with a holder.* Heat the contents of this second tube in a burner flame. Heat gently at first and then strongly for 1 to 2 minutes. Note any change in appearance that occurs. When the heating is complete, place the test tube on a wire gauze. When the test tube and contents have cooled to room temperature, measure their mass and record the result.

Use a spatula to place a sample of the iron filings and sulfur reaction product on a sheet of paper. Break the sample into small pieces, and test with a magnet. Place the test tube and the remaining reaction product in the test tube rack beside the test tube containing the unreacted iron filings and sulfur mixture. *Caution: Perform the following test in a fume hood.* Add 5 or 6 drops of dilute hydrochloric acid to each tube. Carefully check the odor of any gas that is given off by wafting it cautiously toward you.

Material Disposal   Your instructor will tell you how to dispose of the materials.

Experiment 6
Prelaboratory Exercises

1. List some physical properties of

   (a) an ice cube. _____

   (b) water.   _____

   (c) steam.   _____

2. Which of the following are *chemical* changes and which are *physical* changes?

   (a) Boiling water: _____

   (b) Dissolving salt in water: _____

   (c) Rusting of iron: _____

   (d) Evaporation of water: _____

   (e) Cooking an egg: _____

   (f) Burning wood: _____

3. What happens to the reactants when a chemical change occurs?

Experiment 6
Laboratory Report

A. Physical Properties of Matter

Substance	Physical state	Color	Odor	Solubility in water	Effect of magnet
Sulfur	_____	_____	_____	_____	_____
Iron filings	_____	_____	_____	_____	_____
Sodium bicarbonate	_____	_____	_____	_____	_____
Sodium chloride	_____	_____	_____	_____	_____
Sucrose	_____	_____	_____	_____	_____
Sand	_____	_____	_____	_____	_____
Magnesium	_____	_____	_____	_____	_____

B. Causing a Physical Change

Iron filings–sulfur mixture

Appearance: _____

Effect of a magnet on the mixture: _____

Salt-sand mixture

Appearance: _____

Effect of a magnet on the mixture: _____

Residue in the evaporating dish (appearance): _____

Residue on the filter paper (appearance): _____

C. Causing a Chemical Change

Magnesium strip

Appearance: _____

Combustion product (appearance): _____

Action of 6 *M* hydrochloric acid on:

    Magnesium strip _____

    Combustion product _____

Action of heat on sucrose

Change in appearance: _____

Odor: _____

Condensate on test tube: _____

Solubility of sucrose: _____

Solubility of residue: _____

Action of 6 *M* hydrochloric acid on sodium bicarbonate: _____

_____

D. Conservation of Mass

Mass of test tube and iron
filings–sulfur mixture before heating: _____

Mass of test tube and iron
filings–sulfur mixture after heating: _____

Mass difference: _____

Describe what you observed when the iron filings–sulfur mixture was heated:

_____

_____

Effect of magnet on the reaction product: _____

Addition of HCl to unheated reaction mixture:

Odor: _____

Addition of HCl to reaction product:

Odor: _____

Postlaboratory Exercises

1. Did a chemical change occur when iron filings and sulfur were mixed? What evidence was there to support your answer?

2. What type of change occurred when water was added to the salt-sand mixture?

3. How did the substances recovered from the salt-sand mixture compare with the substances used in making the mixture?

4. What was the residue left after sucrose was heated?

5. Did iron filings and sulfur change chemically during the heating process? What evidence do you have to support your answer?

6. Is the reaction of sodium bicarbonate with hydrochloric acid endothermic or exothermic?

7. What is the name of the gas produced in the reaction between sodium bicarbonate and hydrochloric acid?

Identification of Some Important Anions and Cations

Qualitative analysis is the testing of a sample of matter to determine its composition. Qualitative analysis, applied by scientists over many years, revealed the components of living things. In this experiment you will become familiar with tests for several *anions* (negatively charged ions) and *cations* (positively charged ions) in solution. You will then do tests to determine which ions are present in a solution of unknown composition.

Qualitative analysis for ions is based on the fact that no two ions behave identically in all their chemical reactions. Each ion reacts in its own characteristic way. In this exercise you will identify the following anions: chloride, sulfate, carbonate, bicarbonate, and phosphate. You also will identify the following cations: iron, sodium, potassium, calcium, and ammonium.

Some of the identifying characteristics you should look for in doing the tests include (1) a color change in the solution, (2) the evolution of a gaseous product, (3) the formation of a precipitate, and (4) a specific color in a flame test.

Chloride Ion Test.   When a solution of silver nitrate is added to a solution containing chloride ions and nitric acid, a heavy white precipitate of silver chloride forms. The equation for the reaction is

$$Ag^+(aq) + Cl^-(aq) \longrightarrow AgCl(s)$$
$$\text{White}$$
$$\text{precipitate}$$

Sulfate Ion Test.   A white precipitate of barium sulfate is formed in the presence of hydrochloric acid when a solution of barium chloride is added to a solution containing sulfate ions. The equation for the reaction is

$$Ba^{2+}(aq) + SO_4^{2-}(aq) \longrightarrow BaSO_4(s)$$
$$\text{White}$$
$$\text{precipitate}$$

Carbonate Ion and Bicarbonate Ion Test.   The addition of hydrochloric acid to solutions containing carbonate ions or bicarbonate ions or to solid samples of carbonates and bicarbonates causes rapid evolution of carbon dioxide gas. The equations for the reaction of acid with these ions are

$$H^+(aq) + HCO_3^-(aq) \longrightarrow H_2O(l) + CO_2(g)$$
$$2H^+(aq) + CO_3^{2-}(aq) \longrightarrow H_2O(l) + CO_2(g)$$

Phosphate Ion Test.   A bright yellow precipitate of ammonium phosphomolybdate $[(NH_4)_3PO_4 \cdot 12MoO_4]$ is formed when a solution containing phosphate ions is heated with a solution of ammonium molybdate $[(NH_4)_2MoO_4]$ and dilute nitric acid. The yellow precipitate is extremely insoluble in nitric acid.

Ferric Ion Test. The blood-red color of the complex ion $Fe(SCN)^{2+}$ is obtained when a solution of potassium thiocyanate is added to an acidified solution containing ferric ions [iron(III) ions]. The equation for the reaction is

$$Fe^{3+}(aq) + SCN^-(aq) \longrightarrow [Fe(SCN)]^{2+}(aq)$$

Blood-red color

Sodium Ion Test. Sodium ion is identified by the intense yellow color it produces in flame test.

Potassium Ion Test. Potassium ion is identified by the violet color it produces in flame test.

Calcium Ion Test. When a solution of sodium oxalate ($Na_2C_2O_4$) is added to a solution containing calcium ions, a white precipitate of calcium oxalate (CaC_2O_4) forms:

$$Ca^{2+}(aq) + C_2O_4^{2-}(aq) \longrightarrow CaC_2O_4(s)$$

White
precipitate

Calcium ion also gives an orange-red color in flame test.

Ammonium Ion Test. When a strong base such as sodium hydroxide is added to a solution containing ammonium ions, the ammonium ions are converted to ammonia. Ammonia is easily detected by its odor. The equation for the reaction is

$$NH_4^+(aq) + OH^-(aq) \longrightarrow H_2O(l) + NH_3(g)$$

Experiment 7.1 Tests for Anions

Hypothesis

No two anions behave identically in all their chemical reactions.

Objectives

1. To identify anions in solution using simple chemical tests.
2. To use qualitative tests to identify the anions in an unknown solution.

SAFETY PRECAUTIONS

- Wear safety goggles at all times while in the laboratory.
- Long hair must be pinned or tied back and loose clothing secured when you are working with flames.
- Keep flammable substances away from open flames.
- Nitric and hydrochloric acids are damaging to the skin and clothing. Wash off immediately with water if they are spilled, and inform the instructor.
- Barium chloride is toxic. Exercise caution and wash after use.

Materials and Equipment

0.1 M Silver nitrate, 0.1 M sodium sulfate, 0.1 M barium chloride, 0.1 M sodium bicarbonate, 0.05 M sodium phosphate, 0.1 M ammonium molybdate, 0.1 M sodium chloride, 6 M nitric acid, 6 M hydrochloric acid, unknown solutions, high-purity water (distilled or deionized), small test tubes, test tube rack, 25-mL graduated cylinder, 250-mL beaker, dropper pipet, and water bath (ring stand, ring clamp, wire gauze, burner, 250-mL beaker)

Procedure

Use only high-purity water for rinsing glassware and diluting solutions in this experiment. Tap water contains ions that will interfere with your tests and give misleading information.

A. Test for Chloride Ion. Clean two small test tubes, and rinse them with high-purity water. To test tube 1 add 2 mL of sodium chloride solution. To test tube 2 add 2 mL of the unknown solution (1 mL is about 20 drops; 2 mL fills a small test tube to a depth of about 2 cm). Add about 2 mL of dilute nitric acid to each tube, and shake gently to mix the contents. Then add 10 drops of silver nitrate solution to each tube. Shake to mix the solutions, and record your observations and conclusions in the data table.

B. Test for Sulfate Ion. Prepare two small test tubes. To test tube 1, add 2 mL of sodium sulfate solution; to test tube 2, add 2 mL of the unknown. Add 2 mL of 6 M hydrochloric acid to each tube, and shake gently to mix the contents. Then add about 10 drops of barium chloride solution to each tube, shake the solutions, and report your observations and conclusions in the data table.

C. Test for Bicarbonate Ion. Prepare two small test tubes. To test tube 1, add 2 mL of sodium bicarbonate; to tube 2, add 2 mL of the unknown. Add 2 mL of 6 M hydrochloric acid to each solution, and record the results in the data table.

D. Test for Phosphate Ion. Prepare two small test tubes. To test tube 1, add 2 mL of sodium phosphate; to tube 2, add 2 mL of the unknown. Add about 1 mL of dilute nitric acid and 10 drops of 0.1 M ammonium molybdate solution to each tube, and shake gently to mix the contents. Place the test tubes in a boiling water bath for about 5 minutes. Remove the tubes from the water bath, and then let them stand in the test tube rack for 10 minutes longer. Record your results.

Material Disposal

Your instructor will tell you how to dispose of the materials.

Experiment 7.2   Tests for Cations

Hypothesis

No two cations behave identically in their chemical reactions.

Objectives

1. To identify cations in solution using simple chemical tests.
2. To use qualitative tests to identify the cations in an unknown solution.

SAFETY PRECAUTIONS	• Wear safety goggles at all times while in the laboratory. • Long hair must be pinned or tied back and loose clothing secured when you are working with flames. • Keep flammable substances away from open flames. • Nitric and hydrochloric acids and sodium hydroxide are damaging to the skin and clothing. Wash off immediately with water if they are spilled, and inform the instructor.

Materials and Equipment

0.1 M iron(III) sulfate (ferric sulfate), 0.1 M sodium chloride, 0.1 M potassium thiocyanate, 0.1 M potassium chloride, 0.1 M calcium nitrate, 0.1 M sodium oxalate, 0.1 M ammonium nitrate, unknown solution, dilute hydrochloric acid, dilute sulfuric acid, dilute sodium hydroxide, flame test wire (10-cm length of nichrome wire), cobalt-blue glass, small test tubes, test tube rack, red litmus paper, test tube holder, 100-mL beaker, crucible tongs, and water bath (ring stand, ring clamp, wire gauze, burner, 250-mL beaker

Procedure

A. Test for Ferric Ion. Prepare two test tubes. To test tube 1, add 2 mL of ferric sulfate solution; to tube 2, add 2 mL of the unknown solution. Add 5 drops of dilute sulfuric acid and 5 drops of potassium thiocyanate solution to each tube, and shake gently to mix the contents. Record your observations and conclusions in the data table.

B. Test for Sodium Ion. The presence of sodium ion is determined with a flame test. Prepare two test tubes. To test tube 1, add 2 mL of sodium chloride solution; to tube 2, add 2 mL of the unknown. Add 3 drops of 6 *M* hydrochloric acid to each tube, and shake to mix the solutions.

Grasp one end of a 10-cm length of nichrome wire with a pair of crucible tongs. Clean the flame test wire by heating the other end in a hot burner flame and dipping it, while it is still hot, into 6 *M* hydrochloric acid in a small beaker. Reheat the wire in the flame, and dip it into the hydrochloric acid again. Do this several times until the flame remains almost colorless when the wire is inserted.

Dip the wire into the solution in tube 1, and then hold it in the hot burner flame. Record the result. After cleaning the wire thoroughly, test the unknown solution. Record the results. (Since it is easy to contaminate test solutions with sodium ions, a faint yellow flame is not considered a positive test for sodium.)

C. Test for Potassium Ion. Like sodium, potassium is detected with a flame test. Prepare two test tubes. To test tube 1, add 2 mL of potassium chloride solution; to tube 2, add 2 mL of the unknown. Add 3 drops of 6 *M* hydrochloric acid to each tube, and shake to mix.

Clean your flame test wire, dip it into tube 1, and insert it in a hot burner flame. Clean the wire, and test the unknown. Record your results. If your solution contains sodium ions, the bright yellow sodium flame will obscure any violet color due to potassium. The bright yellow of the sodium flame can be filtered out by viewing the flame through a piece of cobalt-blue glass. Only the violet color of the potassium flame is visible through cobalt-blue glass.

D. Test for Calcium Ion. Prepare two test tubes. To test tube 1, add 2 mL of calcium nitrate solution; to tube 2, add 2 mL of the unknown solution. Add 10 drops of sodium oxalate solution to each tube, and warm the tubes in a boiling water bath for a few minutes. Record your observations and conclusions in the data table.

You also can do a flame test on new samples to confirm the presence of calcium. The calcium flame is an orange-red color.

E. Test for Ammonium Ion. Prepare two test tubes. To test tube 1, add 2 mL of ammonium nitrate; to tube 2, add 2 mL of the unknown. Add a few drops of dilute sodium hydroxide solution to each tube. Gently warm the contents of each tube while holding a piece of moistened red litmus paper at the mouth of the tube. Do not let the solution boil; otherwise, the sodium hydroxide will splatter the litmus paper and spoil the test. You also may smell the vapors coming out of the tube by cautiously wafting them toward you. Report your observations in the data table.

Material Disposal

Your instructor will tell you how to dispose of the materials.

Experiment 7
Prelaboratory Exercises

1. Name the following ions, and identify each as a cation or anion.

CO_3^{2-}: _____ _____

NH_4^+: _____ _____

Mg^{2+}: _____ _____

OH^-: _____ _____

NO_3^-: _____ _____

2. Write the chemical formula for each of the following compounds.

Ammonium sulfate: _____

Barium nitrate: _____

Iron(III) phosphate: _____

Potassium oxalate: _____

Sodium phosphate: _____

3. Name the following compounds.

NH_4Cl: _____

K_2CO_3: _____

$Ca(NO_3)_2$: _____

$NaHCO_3$: _____

$FeCl_3$: _____

Experiment 7.1   Tests for Anions
Laboratory Report

A. Solution   **Observations**   **Conclusion**

Sodium chloride
(NaCl)   _____   _____

Unknown   _____   _____

B. Solution   **Observations**   **Conclusion**

Sodium sulfate
(Na_2SO_4)   _____   _____

Unknown   _____   _____

C. Solution   **Observations**   **Conclusion**

Sodium
bicarbonate
($NaHCO_3$)   _____   _____

Unknown   _____   _____

D. Solution   **Observations**   **Conclusion**

Sodium phosphate
(Na_3PO_4)   _____   _____

Unknown   _____   _____

The anions identified in the unknown are _____.

Postlaboratory Exercises

1. A test solution made with dilute nitric acid gives a white precipitate when treated
   with a few drops of silver nitrate. Name the anion present in the test solution.

2. You suspect a sample of high-purity water is contaminated with sulfate ions. How would you test the water to confirm your suspicions?

3. How would you test a sample of urine for (a) phosphate ions and (b) chloride ions?

Experiment 7.2   Tests for Cations
Laboratory Report

A. Solution   **Observations**   **Conclusion**

Iron(III) sulfate
$[Fe_2(SO_4)_3]$ _____   _____

Unknown   _____   _____

B. Solution   **Observations**   **Conclusion**

Sodium chloride
(NaCl)   _____   _____

Unknown   _____   _____

C. Solution   **Observations**   **Conclusion**

Potassium chloride
(KCl)   _____   _____

Unknown   _____   _____

D. Solution   **Observations**   **Conclusion**

Calcium nitrate
$[Ca(NO_3)_2]$ _____   _____

Unknown   _____   _____

E. Solution   **Observations**   **Conclusion**

Ammonium nitrate
(NH_4NO_3) _____   _____

Unknown   _____   _____

The cations identified in the unknown are _____ .

Postlaboratory Exercises

1. Water sample A is contaminated with either sodium ions or potassium ions. Water sample B is contaminated with either sulfate ions or chloride ions. Describe the tests you would perform to identify the contaminating ions in the water samples.

2. Write the chemical formulas for the following compounds.

   Iron(II) sulfate: _____

   Iron(III) sulfate: _____

3. How would you test a sample of urine for calcium ions?

Balanced Chemical Equations and Stoichiometry

Chemical reactions are represented by balanced equations. In a balanced equation, each side of the equation must show the same number of atoms of each element because the law of conservation of matter must be obeyed. Balanced chemical equations are extremely useful. Using them, we can determine the quantities of reactants to mix and calculate the quantities of products to expect from a reaction. Consider the balanced equation

$$Ba(NO_3)_2(aq) + K_2SO_4(aq) \longrightarrow BaSO_4(s) + 2KNO_3(aq)$$

We can interpret this equation as follows: one formula unit of barium nitrate [$Ba(NO_3)_2$] reacts with one formula unit of potassium sulfate (K_2SO_4) to produce one formula unit of barium sulfate ($BaSO_4$) and two formula units of potassium nitrate (KNO_3). This interpretation is not very useful because we do not carry out reactions in the laboratory using single formula units or single molecules of compounds. Instead, we use moles. We know that one mole of any substance contains the same number of formula units or molecules as one mole of any other substance. We can translate the equation as

$$1 \text{ mol } Ba(NO_3)_2 + 1 \text{ mol } K_2SO_4 \longrightarrow 1 \text{ mol } BaSO_4 + 2 \text{ mol } KNO_3$$

Since one mole is the molar mass of a substance, one mole of $Ba(NO_3)_2$ has a mass of 261.3 g, one mole of K_2SO_4 has a mass of 174.3 g, one mole of $BaSO_4$ has a mass of 233.4 g, and two moles of KNO_3 have a mass of 202.2 g. Thus we also have the mass relationship

$$261.3 \text{ g } Ba(NO_3)_2 + 174.3 \text{ g } K_2SO_4 \longrightarrow 233.4 \text{ g } BaSO_4 + 202.2 \text{ g } KNO_3$$

Because we started with a balanced equation, the total mass of all the reactants (261.3 g + 174.3 g = 435.6 g) equals the total mass of all the products (233.4 g + 202.2 g = 435.6 g), and mass is conserved. The law of conservation of matter holds true.

When you have a balanced chemical equation and know the quantity of one substance in a reaction, you can calculate the quantity of any other substance. Calculations using balanced equations are called *stoichiometric calculations*.

In this experiment you will examine the quantitative relationship between the reactants barium nitrate and potassium sulfate and the product barium sulfate. You will make use of the insolubility of barium sulfate to separate it from the reaction mixture by filtration.

Hypotheses

1. We can calculate the quantities of reactants needed to carry out chemical reactions using a balanced chemical equation.
2. If we know the quantities of reactants used in a chemical reaction, we can calculate the quantities of products we should get.

1. To examine the quantitative relationship between reactants and products in a chemical reaction.
2. To verify the law of conservation of mass.
3. To show how a balanced chemical equation gives the relationship between moles of reactants and moles of products.

SAFETY PRECAUTIONS

- **Wear safety goggles at all times while in the laboratory.**
- **Long hair must be pinned or tied back and loose clothing secured when you are working with flames.**
- **Keep flammable substances away from open flames.**
- **Nitric acid is damaging to the skin and clothing. Wash off immediately with water if it is spilled, and inform the instructor.**
- **Barium nitrate is toxic. Exercise caution and wash your hands after use.**

Materials and Equipment

Barium nitrate, anhydrous potassium sulfate, dilute nitric acid, acetone, plastic wash bottle, high-purity water, 250-mL beaker, 100-mL beaker, glass rod, rubber police-man, watch glass, ring stand, ring support, filter funnel, fine filter paper (such as Whatman no. 5 or no. 42), spatula, tripod, laboratory balance, and steam bath

Procedure

From the balanced chemical equation we know that barium nitrate and potassium sulfate react in a 1:1 ratio to produce one mole of barium sulfate. In this exercise the reactants $Ba(NO_3)_2$ and K_2SO_4 will be mixed in a 1:1 mole ratio. The quantity of $BaSO_4$ produced will be measured, and its mass will be compared with the value calculated from the mass relationship of the reactants in the balanced equation.

1. Measure the mass of a clean, dry 250-mL beaker to an accuracy of 0.01 g. Now measure 2.60 ± 0.05 g of $Ba(NO_3)_2$, to an accuracy of 0.01 g, into the beaker. Calculate the number of moles of $Ba(NO_3)_2$ in your mass of $Ba(NO_3)_2$. Add about 100 mL of high-purity water and a few drops of dilute nitric acid to the $Ba(NO_3)_2$. Heat the mixture over a burner flame, and stir to dissolve the $Ba(NO_3)_2$ using a clean glass rod fitted with a rubber policeman. Do not boil.

2. Since $Ba(NO_3)_2$ and K_2SO_4 react in a 1:1 ratio, the number of moles of K_2SO_4 required for complete reaction with $Ba(NO_3)_2$ is the same as the number of moles of $Ba(NO_3)_2$ in solution. Calculate the number of grams of K_2SO_4 required to react with the $Ba(NO_3)_2$, and enter the result in the data table.

3. Measure the calculated amount of K_2SO_4 to an accuracy of 0.01 g into a 100-mL beaker whose mass is known accurately. Add about 50 mL of high-purity water. Heat the mixture over a burner flame, and stir to dissolve the K_2SO_4 using a clean glass rod fitted with a rubber policeman. Do not boil.

Slowly pour the hot K_2SO_4 solution into the hot $Ba(NO_3)_2$ solution with stirring. Wash the residual solution from the 100-mL beaker into the 250-mL beaker with a small volume of high-purity water from a wash bottle. Cover the larger beaker with a watch glass, and put it on a steam bath for about 15 to 30 minutes to allow the precipitate to coagulate and settle. If you do not have a steam bath, you may warm the beaker on a wire gauze over a very low burner flame or a hotplate. Do not boil.

4. While the reaction mixture is heating, set up a filter funnel and ring stand for gravity filtration (review Experiment 1.5). Remove the beaker containing the reaction mixture from the steam bath, and put it on a wire gauze to cool for 5 to 10 min-

utes. (If possible, to make the filtering process more efficient and quantitative, the reaction mixture should be left to stand undisturbed for at least 24 hours at room temperature before proceeding with the filtration.) Determine the mass of a sheet of filter paper to an accuracy of 0.01 g, and record its mass in the data table. Place the filter paper in the filter funnel. Filter the reaction mixture using a glass rod to direct the flow of liquid into the funnel. Be careful not to overfill the filter funnel during the filtration. The $BaSO_4$ precipitate remaining in the beaker should be washed carefully into the funnel with a jet of high-purity water from your wash bottle. Any precipitate that sticks to the walls of the beaker should be dislodged by rubbing it with the rubber policeman at the end of a glass rod and then washed out with high-purity water. Wash the precipitate on the filter paper with two 10-mL portions of water. Dry the precipitate by washing it with three 5-mL portions of acetone. When the final portion of acetone has passed through the filter paper, carefully remove the filter paper and precipitate from the funnel, open it flat, and allow the residual acetone to evaporate. Discard the filtrate. Accurately determine the mass of a clean, dry watch glass. Put the filter paper and precipitated $BaSO_4$ onto the watch glass, and measure the mass of the watch glass and its contents.

5. Calculate the theoretical yield of $BaSO_4$. Remember that 1 mol of $Ba(NO_3)_2$ reacts with 1 mol of K_2SO_4 to produce 1 mol of $BaSO_4$.

Material Disposal   Your instructor will tell you how to dispose of the materials.

Experiment 8
Prelaboratory Exercises

1. Write the chemical formula of ammonium sulfate. _____

2. What is the molar mass of this compound? _____

3. How many moles is 3.6 g H_2O? _____

4. How many grams is 0.20 mol NaCl? _____

5. Write a balanced chemical equation for the reaction of calcium chloride with sodium carbonate in aqueous solution. The products are a solution of sodium chloride and a precipitate of calcium carbonate.

_____ + _____ ⟶ _____ + _____

Experiment 8
Laboratory Report

1. Mass of empty beaker: ——————— g

   Mass of beaker and $Ba(NO_3)_2$:   ——————— g

   Mass of $Ba(NO_3)_2$:   ——————— g

   Molar mass of $Ba(NO_3)_2$:   ——————— g/mol

$$\text{Moles of } Ba(NO_3)_2 = \frac{\text{mass of } Ba(NO_3)_2}{\text{molar mass}} = \frac{\text{———————— g}}{\text{———————— g/mol}}$$

$$= \text{————————— mol}$$

2. Moles of $Ba(NO_3)_2$ in solution: ——————— mol

   Moles of K_2SO_4 required: ——————— mol

   Molar mass of K_2SO_4: ——————— g/mol

$$\text{Mass of } K_2SO_4 \text{ required} = \text{moles} \times \text{molar mass}$$

$$= \text{————} \text{ mol} \times \text{————} \text{ g/mol} = \text{————} \text{ g}$$

3. Mass of empty beaker: ——————— g

   Mass of beaker and K_2SO_4:   ——————— g

   Mass of K_2SO_4:   ——————— g

4. Mass of filter paper: ——————— g

   Mass of watch glass: ——————— g

   Mass of filter paper and watch glass: ——————— g

   Mass of watch glass, filter paper, and $BaSO_4$:   ——————— g

   Mass of $BaSO_4$:   ——————— g

5. Moles of $Ba(NO_3)_2$ used: ——————— mol

   Moles of $BaSO_4$ produced: ——————— mol

   Molar mass of $BaSO_4$:   ——————— g/mol

Theoretical yield of $BaSO_4$ = moles $BaSO_4$ × molar mass $BaSO_4$

= _____ mol × _____ g/mol = _____ g

Compare your actual yield with the theoretical value.

Postlaboratory Exercises

1. If your actual yield of $BaSO_4$ differs by more than 0.05 g from the theoretical yield, how might you account for the difference?

2. Balance the following equation, and then calculate the number of moles of silver chloride that precipitates when 4.0 mol $AgNO_3$ reacts with 4.0 mol $CaCl_2$.

$$AgNO_3(aq) + CaCl_2(aq) \longrightarrow AgCl(s) + Ca(NO_3)_2(aq)$$

Factors That Affect the Rate of a Chemical Reaction

The rates of chemical reactions are influenced by temperature, the presence of catalysts, concentration of reactants, and the particle size or the surface area of the reacting species. To see how these factors influence reaction rates, let us examine how reactions occur.

Molecules must collide to react. The colliding particles must have sufficient energy to enable bond-breaking and bond-making processes to occur. The minimum energy requirement for the colliding particles is the activation energy, an energy barrier that reactants must cross to be converted to products.

Raising the temperature normally speeds up a reaction, and lowering the temperature usually slows it down. At high temperatures, the motions of the reacting particles are more chaotic and energetic. The frequency of collisions and the number of reactant molecules energetic enough to cross the energy barrier to products therefore increase.

Catalysts are substances that speed up chemical reactions by providing an alternative reaction path of lower activation energy that is unavailable in the absence of the catalyst. Thus, at a given temperature, a larger fraction of the reactants can cross the energy barrier to products in the presence of a catalyst. It is important to remember that although a catalyst speeds up a reaction, it cannot turn an energetically unfavorable reaction into a spontaneous reaction.

Increasing the concentration of reactants increases the frequency of collisions between reacting particles and therefore increases the reaction rate.

For a given mass, the smaller the particle size, the greater the surface area, the greater the collision frequency, and the faster the reaction.

We will examine the effects of temperature, catalysts, reactant concentration, and particle size and surface area on reaction rates in this experiment.

Hypothesis

The rate of a chemical reaction can be affected by a number of factors.

Objectives

1. To determine the effect of reactant concentration on reaction rate.
2. To demonstrate the effect of temperature on reaction rate.
3. To determine the effect of a catalyst on reaction rate.
4. To demonstrate the effect of particle size and surface area on reaction rate.

SAFETY PRECAUTIONS	• Wear safety goggles at all times while in the laboratory. • Long hair must be pinned or tied back and loose clothing secured when you are working with flames. • Keep flammable substances away from open flames.

0.1 *M* Iron(III) chloride, 0.1 *M* iron(III) nitrate, 0.1 *M* sodium chloride, 0.1 *M* calcium chloride, 0.1 *M* potassium nitrate, 0.1 *M* manganese chloride, 3% hydrogen peroxide solution, concentrated hydrochloric acid, 6 *M* hydrochloric acid, 1 *M* hydrochloric acid, 0.1 *M* hydrochloric acid, oxygen gas (cylinder), zinc strips, powdered zinc, high-purity water, wood splint, steel wool, 10-mL graduated cylinder, 100-mL graduated cylinder, metal cutting scissors, medium test tubes, glass stirring rod, 250-mL beaker, laboratory balance, test tube rack, watch glass, tongs, thermometer, 250-mL polyethylene bottle, and water bath (ring stand, ring clamp, wire gauze, burner, 250-mL beaker)

Procedure

A. Effect of Temperature on Reaction Rate. You will use the reaction of zinc metal with hydrochloric acid to study the effect of temperature on reaction rate. Pour 5 mL of 6 *M* hydrochloric acid, measured with a 10-mL graduated cylinder, into each of three clean test tubes. Place one of the tubes in a 250-mL beaker containing an ice-water mixture, place another in a water bath at 50 °C, and place the third tube in a test tube rack at room temperature. Allow about 5 minutes for the tubes to reach the temperature of their surroundings. Clean a zinc strip with steel wool, and cut three pieces of zinc approximately 1 cm × 1 cm × 0.2 mm thick. Record the time as you drop a piece of zinc into each of the three test tubes, and record the time when each reaction ceases—when bubbling stops or no zinc remains. Hydrogen gas is a product of the reaction. Hydrogen can be detected by bringing a burning wood splint to the mouth of the test tube. A popping sound indicates the presence of hydrogen. Record your observations in the data table.

B. Effect of a Catalyst on Reaction Rate. The rate of decomposition of hydrogen peroxide (H_2O_2) into water and oxygen will be used to study the effect of catalysts on a chemical reaction. The reaction is followed by noting the rate at which oxygen gas is evolved.

Measure 90 mL of high-purity water into a clean 100-mL graduated cylinder, and add 10 mL of 3% hydrogen peroxide solution. Pour this solution into a clean 250-mL bottle, and label it 0.3% H_2O_2. This is your test solution.

Clean seven test tubes and a 10-mL graduated cylinder, and rinse each with a 2-mL portion of 0.3% H_2O_2. Discard the rinse solutions. Use the graduated cylinder to measure 5 mL of 0.3% H_2O_2 into each of the test tubes, and place the tubes in a rack. Test solutions of compounds listed in the data table for catalytic activity by adding 5 drops of each solution to separate tubes containing 0.3% H_2O_2. Gently shake each tube to mix its contents. Observe each solution carefully for several minutes. Use the terms *fast, slow, very slow,* or *none* to describe the rate of oxygen evolution and the words *high, low,* or *none* to describe the catalytic activity. Report the rate of oxygen gas evolution and the catalytic activity for each in the data table.

All the substances tested for catalytic activity are ionic, and each produces an anion and a cation in solution. On the basis of your results, classify the individual ions according to their catalytic activity, and complete the data table by entering the name and symbol for each ion in the appropriate category.

C. Effect of Concentration on Reaction Rate. The reaction of zinc metal with hydrochloric acid solutions and the combustion of substances in oxygen will be used to study the effect of concentration on a reaction rate.

Using a clean 10-mL graduated cylinder, pour 5 mL of each of the following hydrochloric acid solutions into separate clean test tubes: 0.1 *M* HCl, 1 *M* HCl, 6 *M* HCl, and concentrated HCl. Clean a zinc strip with steel wool, and cut four small pieces of approximately the same size (about 1 cm × 1 cm). Record the time, and drop a piece of zinc into each of the acid solutions. Record the time each reaction ceases, and report your observations in the data table.

Purge two clean, dry 250-mL beakers with oxygen gas from a cylinder (your instructor will supervise this operation), and cover them with watch glasses. Hold a wood splint in a pair of tongs, and light it. Blow out the flame and quickly plunge the glowing splint into the oxygen in one of the beakers. Then hold a *small* piece of fluffed-up steel wool in a pair of tongs. Heat the steel wool in a burner flame, and while it is still glowing, plunge it into the oxygen in the second beaker. Record your observations in the data table.

D. Effect of Particle Size or Surface Area.
The reaction of zinc metal with hydrochloric acid will be used to study the effect of particle size and surface area on the rate of a reaction.

Cut a piece of metal about 1 cm × 1 cm × 0.2 mm from a polished sheet of zinc, and determine its mass to the nearest 0.01 g. Place the metal in a clean, dry test tube. Measure an equal mass of powdered zinc into another clean, dry test tube. *Caution: Finely divided metals are flammable.* Put both tubes in a test tube rack, and add 5 mL of 1 M hydrochloric acid to each. Observe the reactions for several minutes, and record your observations in the data table.

Material Disposal   Your instructor will tell you how to dispose of the materials.

Experiment 9
Prelaboratory Exercises

1. Give two ways to speed up the rate of a chemical reaction.

2. Comment on the statement: "Catalysts are substances that speed up chemical reactions and make energetically unfavorable reactions occur."

3. Sketch an energy-level diagram for the conversion of reactants to products in an endothermic reaction. Label the activation energy barrier.

4. Lowering the temperature usually slows down a chemical reaction. Explain.

Experiment 9
Laboratory Report

A.

Reaction conditions	Reaction started (time)	Reaction ceased (time)	Reaction duration (min)	Test for hydrogen
Ice water, 0 °C	_____	_____	_____	_____
Room temperature ____°C	_____	_____	_____	_____
Hot water, 50 °C	_____	_____	_____	_____

B.

Test	Substance tested						
	HCl 6 M	FeCl$_3$ 0.1 M	NaCl 0.1 M	Fe(NO$_3$)$_3$ 0.1 M	CaCl$_2$ 0.1 M	KNO$_3$ 0.1 M	MnCl$_2$ 0.1 M
Oxygen evolution	_____	_____	_____	_____	_____	_____	_____
Catalytic activity	_____	_____	_____	_____	_____	_____	_____

Catalytic activity	Name	Ion symbol
High	_____	_____
Low	_____	_____
None	_____	_____

C.

Reaction condition	Reaction started (time)	Reaction ceased (time)	Reaction duration (s)	Observation
0.1 M HCl	_____	_____	_____	_____
1 M HCl	_____	_____	_____	_____
6 M HCl	_____	_____	_____	_____
Conc. HCl	_____	_____	_____	_____

| | Observations | |
Substance tested	Combustion in air (20% oxygen)	Combustion in pure oxygen
Wood splint	_____	_____
Steel wool	_____	_____

D. **Substance tested**   **Observations**

Sheet zinc   _____

_____

Powdered zinc   _____

_____

Postlaboratory Exercises

1. Write a balanced equation for the chemical reaction that occurs between zinc and hydrochloric acid.

   _____ + _____ $\longrightarrow$ _____ + _____

2. Many reaction rates approximately double for every 10 °C increase in temperature. How do your results from the temperature experiment compare with this general statement?

3. Write a balanced equation for the decomposition of hydrogen peroxide to oxygen gas and water.

   _____ $\longrightarrow$ _____ + _____

4. Assume that steel wool is iron (Fe) and that the combustion product is iron(III) oxide (Fe_2O_3). Write a balanced equation for the combustion of steel wool in oxygen.

   _____ + _____ $\longrightarrow$ _____

5. Why must you never smoke or cause a spark near a patient in an oxygen tent?

6. Explain any observed difference in the rates of reaction of zinc sheet metal and zinc dust with hydrochloric acid.

7. On the basis of your observations concerning particle size and reaction rate, explain why the atmosphere in flour mills and coal mines is potentially explosive.

8. Explain the difference in the rates of combustion of a wood splint and steel wool in 20% oxygen (air) with the rates of combustion of the same substances in 100% oxygen.

9. From your observations, what can you conclude about the effect of concentration on the rate of a reaction?

Disturbing the Position of Equilibrium: Le Châtelier's Principle

Many of the reactions you have studied go to completion, that is, reactants are totally converted to products. We made use of this fact in the formation of barium sulfate in Experiment 8. Many other reactions are reversible, however. In reversible reactions, the forward reaction (the conversion of reactants to products) and the backward reaction (the conversion of products to reactants) occur simultaneously. The reaction has reached equilibrium at the point at which the forward and backward reaction rates are the same. At equilibrium, the concentrations of reactants and products do not change, but the forward and backward reactions continue to occur.

A saturated solution is an example of a physical system in a state of dynamic equilibrium. In a system containing a soluble substance and a solution saturated with the substance, the solid and the solution are in equilibrium. That is, the solid goes into solution at the same rate that solid deposits from solution. The equation for the equilibrium condition in a saturated solution of sodium chloride is represented by

$$NaCl(s) \rightleftharpoons Na^+(aq) + Cl^-(aq)$$

Out of solution   In solution

Le Châtelier's principle applies to systems in equilibrium. It states that if a stress is placed on a system at equilibrium, the system will change in the direction that relieves the stress. For example, if a compound containing either sodium ions or chloride ions is added to a saturated solution of sodium chloride, the equilibrium shifts to the left. The added common ion Na^+ or Cl^- puts the stress on the system. The system responds to the stress by depositing solid NaCl from solution. The effect of adding the common ion Na^+ or Cl^- on the equilibrium is called the *common-ion effect*.

Temperature also affects the position of equilibrium. At a given temperature, the quantity of sodium chloride in a saturated solution is constant. At 25 °C, for example, 36 g of NaCl dissolves in 100 mL of water. If the temperature of the solution is lowered, the equilibrium again shifts to the left as the system absorbs the stress. In this case, the stress is the lowering of the temperature, and the system relieves the stress by depositing NaCl from solution.

In our study of Le Châtelier's principle we will impose stresses on physical and chemical systems originally in a state of dynamic equilibrium and examine how the systems act to relieve the stress.

Hypothesis   Changing the conditions of a system in equilibrium places a stress on the system. The position of equilibrium shifts to relieve the stress.

Objective   To demonstrate Le Châtelier's principle by observing the effect of a change in conditions on a system at equilibrium.

Materials and Equipment

Saturated potassium nitrate solution, 0.1 M iron(III) chloride, 0.1 M potassium thiocyanate, sodium chloride crystals, ice, test tubes, test tube rack, 250-mL beaker, spatula, and dropper pipet

Procedure

A. Effect of a Temperature Change on a Physical System.   Place 2 to 3 mL of saturated potassium nitrate solution in a test tube. Add *one crystal* of potassium nitrate to act as a seed crystal. (It should not dissolve. If it does, the solution is not saturated.) Immerse the tube in a beaker of ice water for 10 minutes, and record the result. Remove the tube from the ice water, wipe it dry, and place it in the test tube rack. Record what happens as the solution warms to room temperature.

B. Common Ion Effect on a Chemical System.   Add 1 mL of 0.1 M iron(III) chloride ($FeCl_3$) solution and 1 mL of 0.1 M potassium thiocyanate (KSCN) solution to 50 mL of high-purity water. Shake to mix, and note the color. This is the test solution. It contains ferric ions, thiocyanate ions, and ferrithiocyanate ions in a state of dynamic equilibrium. The equilibrium expression is

$$Fe^{3+} + SCN^- \rightleftharpoons [Fe(SCN)]^{2+}$$

Of these three ions, Fe^{3+} is pale yellow, SCN^- is colorless, and $[Fe(SCN)]^{2+}$ is blood red.

   Pour about 5 mL of the test solution into each of four test tubes. Test tube 1 is the control. To test tube 2, add about 20 drops of 0.1 M iron(III) chloride solution, and mix. To test tube 3, add about 20 drops of 0.1 M potassium thiocyanate solution, and mix. To test tube 4, add about 1 g of solid potassium chloride, and shake to dissolve. Note any changes in color compared with your control.

Material Disposal

Your instructor will tell you how to dispose of the materials.

Experiment 10

Prelaboratory Exercise

1. What is meant by the term *reversible reaction?*

2. Explain the term *dynamic equilibrium.*

3. When carbon dioxide is dissolved in water, some of the molecules react with water to produce carbonic acid. The system eventually reaches a state of dynamic equilibrium that is represented by the equation

$$H_2O + CO_2 \rightleftharpoons H_2CO_3$$

What happens to the position of equilibrium when the concentration of carbon dioxide dissolved in water is increased?

Experiment 10
Laboratory Report

A. Test conditions   **Observations**

Cooling to 0 °C

_____

_____

Warming to
room temperature

_____

_____

B. Tube	**Ions added**	**Observations**
1	Control	_____
		_____
2	_____	_____
		_____
3	_____	_____
		_____
4	_____	_____
		_____

Postlaboratory Exercises

1. (a) What evidence do you have that the equilibrium shifted when saturated
potassium nitrate solution was cooled?

(b) In which direction did the equilibrium shift?

(c) What was the stress on the system?

2. (a) What evidence do you have that the equilibrium shifted when iron(III) chloride was added to the test solution containing iron(III) chloride and potassium thiocyanate?

(b) In which direction did the equilibrium shift?

(c) What ion caused the stress on the system?

(d) Why did the addition of potassium thiocyanate cause the equilibrium to shift the way it did?

(e) What ion caused the shift?

(f) Explain the effect of potassium chloride on the equilibrium of the system.

The Gaseous State: Graham's Law of Diffusion

The kinetic molecular theory proposes that the volume of a gas is mostly empty space in which the molecules of the gas move in continuous, random motion. There is much evidence in support of this theory. For example, when a bottle of perfume is opened in a room, the molecules from this volatile liquid are soon detected at a distance from the bottle. The molecules in the perfume vapor mingle with the molecules in the air, and because of the continuous chaotic motion of the gas molecules, the perfume soon spreads throughout the room. This mingling of gas particles is called *diffusion*.

At a given temperature, all gas molecules have the same kinetic energy. However, because they have different molecular masses, they do not all move at the same speed. Heavier gas molecules move more slowly than lighter gas molecules. Oxygen molecules with a molar mass of 32 amu, for example, move more slowly than hydrogen molecules with a molar mass of 2 amu. Heavier gas molecules therefore diffuse more slowly than lighter gas molecules. The relationship between the mass of a gas molecule and its rate of diffusion is given by *Graham's law of diffusion:* The rates of diffusion of different gases are inversely proportional to the square roots of their molecular masses. The mathematical statement of the law as applied to oxygen and hydrogen is

$$\frac{Rate_{H_2}}{Rate_{O_2}} = \frac{\sqrt{Molar\ mass_{O_2}}}{\sqrt{Molar\ mass_{H_2}}}$$

Substituting the molecular masses gives

$$\frac{Rate_{H_2}}{Rate_{O_2}} = \frac{\sqrt{32.0}}{\sqrt{2.00}} = \frac{5.66}{1.41} = 4.01$$

We see that hydrogen diffuses about four times as fast as oxygen at the same temperature.

In this experiment, the relative rates of diffusion of ammonia gas (NH_3) and hydrogen chloride gas (HCl) will be measured at room temperature.

Hypothesis

The rate of diffusion of a particle in a gas is inversely proportional to the square root of the molecular mass of the particle.

Objectives

1. To measure the rate of diffusion of a gas.
2. To measure the relative rates of diffusion of two gases.
3. To verify Graham's law of diffusion.

Materials and Equipment

Concentrated hydrochloric acid, concentrated ammonia solution, acetone, high-purity water, glass tube (70 cm long × 1 cm diameter), ring stands and clamps, cotton, timer, meter stick, rubber stopper (1 cm diameter), dropper pipets, and 100-mL beaker

Procedure

For good results, the diffusion tube must be clean and dry. Clean the glass tube (the diffusion tube) by washing it in warm soapy water and rinsing it thoroughly with high-purity water. Pour several small volumes of acetone down the tube to remove the water; then use an aspirator to draw air through the tube for several minutes to evaporate the acetone.

Fit cotton plugs snugly into the ends of the diffusion tube, and close each end loosely with a rubber stopper. Use two ring stands and clamps to hold the tube level, as shown in Figure 11.1.

Remove the rubber stoppers. Using dropper pipets, simultaneously add 5 drops of concentrated hydrochloric acid (the source of HCl molecules) to the cotton wad at one end of the tube and 5 drops of concentrated ammonia solution (the source of NH_3 molecules) to the other. Replace the rubber stoppers, and note the time. Watch for the formation of a white deposit inside the tube. As soon as it appears, note the time. Measure to the nearest 0.1 cm the distance from each cotton plug to the center

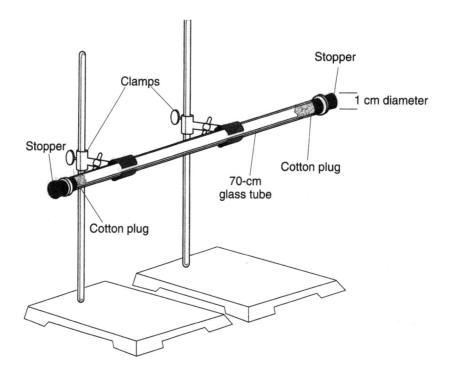

Figure 11.1 Diffusion apparatus.

of the white deposit; these are the distances the HCl and NH$_3$ molecules diffused. Clean the diffusion tube, and repeat the experiment if time permits. Record your results in the data table.

Material Disposal   Your instructor will tell you how to dispose of the materials.

Experiment 11
Prelaboratory Exercises

1. Compare the motion of particles in a gas with the motions of particles in liquids and solids.

2. Would you expect the motions of particles in all states of matter to increase or decrease as the temperature is increased? Explain your answer.

3. Would you expect the particles in chlorine gas to diffuse faster or slower than (a) the particles in argon gas and (b) the particles in nitrogen gas? (Assume the gases are at room temperature.)

4. Calculate how many times faster helium diffuses than oxygen at room temperature.

5. Why does a rubber balloon filled with air remain inflated for a longer period of time than one filled with helium? (*Hint:* Ask yourself why the balloon slowly becomes deflated.)

6. The average speed of a gas particle at room temperature is about 1600 km/h. Why don't the molecules released from a bottle of perfume in New York reach San Francisco, about 5000 km away, 3 hours later?

Experiment 11
Laboratory Report

	Trial 1	Trial 2
Time for appearance of white deposit:	_____ s	_____ s
Distance from HCl plug to white deposit:	_____ cm	_____ cm
Distance from NH_3 plug to white deposit:	_____ cm	_____ cm
Rate of diffusion of HCl (distance/time):	_____	_____
Rate of diffusion of NH_3 (distance/time):	_____	_____

The gas that diffused the fastest was _____.

This gas diffused _____ times faster than the other gas.

Postlaboratory Exercises

1. Using the experimentally determined value for $rate_{NH_3}/rate_{HCl}$ and a molar mass of 17.0 for NH_3, calculate a molar mass for HCl.

2. Write a balanced equation for the reaction that produced the white deposit inside the tube.

3. What changes would you expect to observe if the experiment were repeated at 50 °C?

The Gaseous State: Boyle's Law

We spend our lives in air—a mixture of gases. Anesthetic gases and oxygen used in hospitals are stored under pressure in heavy metal cylinders. Fuel gas is piped to homes or stored in tanks under pressure. There are therefore many reasons why it is important to understand the behavior of these elusive substances.

When the pressure on a gas sample is increased, the volume of the gas decreases. When the pressure on the gas is decreased, its volume increases. A quantitative relationship between the volume of a gas and its pressure was first established by Robert Boyle in 1662. According to *Boyle's law*, the volume of a fixed quantity of gas is inversely proportional to the pressure, provided the temperature remains constant. This law can be expressed mathematically as

$$V \propto \frac{1}{P} \quad \text{or} \quad V = \frac{k}{P}$$

where V is the volume, P is the pressure, and k is a constant that depends on the temperature and the quantity of gas. The second of these expressions can be rearranged to give

$$P \times V = k$$

In other words, the product of the pressure and volume of a fixed mass of gas is constant at constant temperature. Suppose we have two sets of pressure-volume conditions for a given quantity of gas; P_1 and V_1 are the pressure and volume for the first set of conditions, and P_2 and V_2, for the second set of conditions. Then we can write

$$P_1 \times V_1 = k \quad \text{and} \quad P_2 \times V_2 = k$$

Therefore,

$$P_1 \times V_1 = P_2 \times V_2$$

This form of Boyle's law is commonly used for pressure-volume calculations.

In this experiment, you will measure the volume of a fixed quantity of air as the pressure is varied at room temperature.

Hypothesis

The volume of a fixed mass of gas is inversely proportional to the pressure applied to the gas.

Objectives

1. To determine the pressure-volume relationship for a gas at constant temperature.
2. To verify Boyle's law by plotting pressure versus volume to show the inverse relationship.

SAFETY PRECAUTION

· **Wear safety goggles at all times while in the laboratory.**

Acetone, 500-mL filter flask, 50-cm length of glass capillary tubing, plastic tubing, one-holed rubber stopper, 30-mL plastic syringe, dibutyl phthalate, 100-mL graduated cylinder, 500-mL graduated cylinder, silicone grease, barometer, ring stand, utility clamp, meter stick, glass-marking pen, thermometer, and glycerol

Procedure

Select a one-holed rubber stopper to fit the filter flask; the capillary tube must fit snugly into the hole of the stopper. Push a 5-cm length of plastic tubing over the sidearm of a 500-mL filter flask. Close the open end of the plastic tube with your index finger, and fill the flask with water. The bottom of the stopper should be at the water level when it is inserted in the flask (Fig. 12.1).

Carefully pour the water from the filter flask into a 500-mL graduated cylinder. Record the volume of the flask. Rinse the filter flask with several 10-mL portions of acetone, and blow it dry in a stream of air. Use a 50-mL graduated cylinder to measure 50 mL of dibutyl phthalate (DBP). Pour the DBP into the dry filter flask.

Use a glass-marking pen to mark the capillary tube at 1-cm intervals. Lubricate one end of the tube with one or two drops of glycerol, and carefully push it through the hole in the rubber stopper. Insert the rubber stopper containing the capillary tube into the mouth of the filter flask, and adjust the tube so that its lower end is about 5 mm below the surface of the DBP. Apply a thin film of silicone grease to the plunger of the syringe, and push the plunger into the syringe barrel to the 30-mL mark. Insert the end of the syringe into the plastic tubing attached to the filter flask. Support the assembly as shown in Figure 12.2.

Determine the volume occupied by the capillary tube that extends into the filter flask, as shown in the data table. Now determine the volume of air in the apparatus, excluding the volume of the air in the syringe, as shown in the data table. Record the atmospheric (barometric) pressure and room temperature in the data table.

Read the height to which the column of DBP has risen in the capillary tube, and note the volume of air in the syringe barrel. It should be 30 mL; adjust if necessary. Record your measurements in the data table. Now push the plunger to the 25-mL mark. When the level of DBP in the capillary tube comes to rest, read the height of the DBP column, and record the measurement. Repeat the process, at 5-mL intervals, until all the air has been pushed out of the syringe into the flask. Complete the data table.

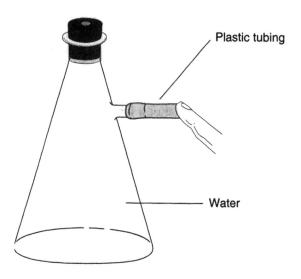

Plastic tubing

Water

Figure 12.1 Measuring the volume of the filter flask.

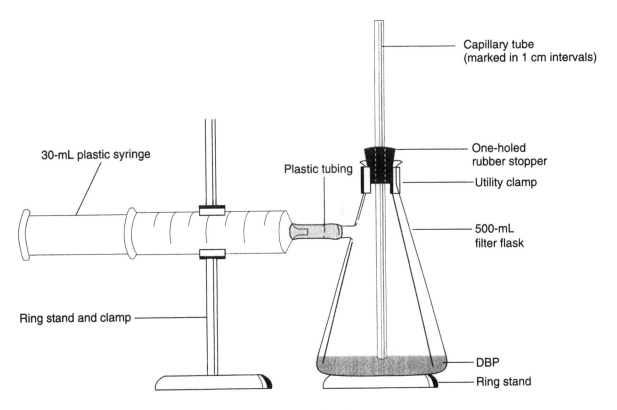

Figure 12.2 *Apparatus for studying pressure-volume relationship of a gas.*

Repeat the experiment by removing the syringe from the plastic tubing, resetting the plunger to the 30-mL mark, and replacing the end of the syringe in the plastic tube.

The density of DBP is 1.05 g/cm^3, and the density of mercury is 13.6 g/cm^3. Therefore, a pressure that supports a 1-cm column of DBP will support a column of mercury only 0.077 cm high. The calculation is done as follows:

$$1 \text{ cm} \times \frac{1.05 \text{ g/cm}^3}{13.6 \text{ g/cm}^3} = 0.077 \text{ cm}$$

To calculate the pressure of each volume of enclosed air in centimeters of mercury, multiply the height of the column of DBP at that volume by 0.077, and add that value to the barometric pressure.

For each set of measurements, calculate the pressure-volume product, and record the result in the data table. Plot pressure versus volume on the graph paper provided. Choose the scales for the axes of the graph to give the largest spread of data points. Draw the smooth line that best fits all your data points.

Material Disposal   Your instructor will tell you how to dispose of the materials.

Experiment 12
Prelaboratory Exercises

1. Name two physical properties of a gas.

2. How does the kinetic molecular theory describe a gas?

3. What is the cause of gas pressure?

The Gaseous State: Charles's Law

When a gas is heated, its volume increases, and when it is cooled, its volume decreases. The quantitative relationship between the temperature of a gas and its volume was determined in the late eighteenth century by Jacques Charles. *Charles's law* states that, at constant pressure, the volume of a given mass of a gas is directly proportional to its Kelvin temperature. This law can be expressed mathematically as

$$V \propto T \quad \text{or} \quad V = k \times T \quad \text{or} \quad \frac{V}{T} = k$$

where V is the volume, T is the temperature on the Kelvin scale, and k is a constant.

If we have two sets of conditions for a given quantity of gas, then we can write

$$\frac{V_1}{T_1} = k \quad \text{and} \quad \frac{V_2}{T_2} = k$$

Therefore,

$$\frac{V_1}{T_1} = \frac{V_2}{T_2}$$

where V_1 and T_1 are the first set of conditions, and V_2 and T_2 are the second set.

In this experiment you will measure the volume of a trapped sample of air at various temperatures. (Actually, you will measure the height of a column of air trapped in a capillary tube. The height of the column of air is directly proportional to its volume.) Pressure will remain constant at the barometric pressure in the laboratory.

Hypothesis

The volume of a given mass of gas varies directly with its Kelvin temperature.

Objectives

1. To determine the volume-temperature relationship of a fixed quantity of gas at constant pressure.
2. To graph volume versus temperature to verify Charles's law.
3. To determine the value of absolute zero.

SAFETY PRECAUTIONS	• **Wear safety goggles at all times while in the laboratory.** • **Long hair must be pinned or tied back and loose clothing secured when you are working with flames.** • **Keep flammable substances away from open flames.**

Materials and Equipment

Dibutyl phthalate, 20-cm glass capillary tube (about 2-mm inside diameter), meter stick, 400-mL beaker, thermometer, small rubber band (to fit around capillary tube), test tube holder, forceps, and water bath (ring stand, ring clamp, watch glass, wire gauze, 250-mL beaker, burner)

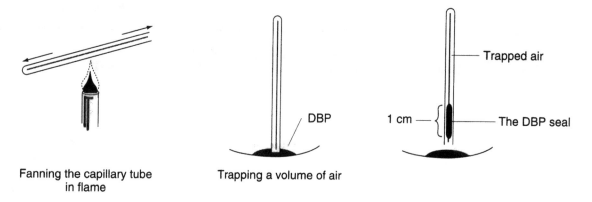

Fanning the capillary tube
in flame

Trapping a volume of air

Trapped air

1 cm

The DBP seal

Figure 13.1 *Preparing the Charles's law tube.*

Procedure

To prepare a Charles's law tube, seal one end of the glass capillary tube by rotating it in a hot flame, and fire polish the open end. Place 2 mL of dibutyl phthalate (DBP) on a clean watch glass. Grasp the Charles's law tube in a test tube holder, and fan it with a hot burner flame for about 20 seconds. Immediately insert the open end of the hot tube into the DBP on the watch glass, and draw about a 1-cm length of the liquid into the capillary tube (Fig. 13.1). Clamp the tube vertically, open end up, on a ring stand, and allow the tube to cool to room temperature. The column of trapped air should be 5 to 10 cm long. Push a small rubber band or a thin slice of rubber tubing over the capillary tube until it is about halfway along the tube; this rubber band will serve as a distance marker.

Suspend the tube vertically, open end up, in a 400-mL beaker containing ice water (Fig. 13.2). *The entire trapped air column must be submerged.* After a few minutes, carefully push the rubber band along the column (you may wish to use for-

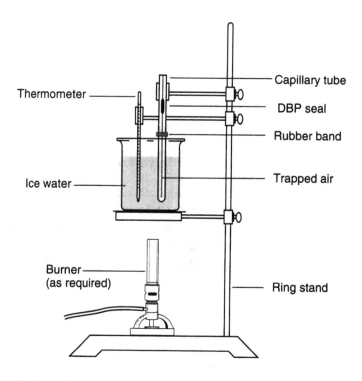

Thermometer

Capillary tube

DBP seal

Rubber band

Ice water

Trapped air

Burner
(as required)

Ring stand

Figure 13.2 *Charles's law apparatus.*

ceps) until the upper edge of the band aligns with the top of the air column. Wait another minute, and make adjustments if necessary. When conditions are steady, measure the temperature of the bath to the nearest 0.1 °C. Remove the tube from the ice-water bath, and holding the tube vertically, measure the length from the bottom of the tube to the top edge of the marker. Record the results. Repeat the procedure using water at room temperature and then at approximately 20 °C intervals up to 100 °C. Move the rubber band to mark the top of the air column at each new temperature. Record the temperature of the water and the height of the column of trapped air in each case. (Your instructor may ask you to use a salt-ice cooling mixture to reach a lower temperature and a hot-oil bath for temperatures above 100 °C.) Complete the data table.

Graph the volume-temperature data as follows: Plot volume versus temperature on the graph paper provided. The horizontal axis is temperature in degrees Kelvin; the vertical axis is the height of the column of air in centimeters. Choose scales that give you the greatest spread of data points. Draw the best straight line through the points.

Plot volume versus temperature as before, but this time label the scale on the temperature axis (the longer, horizontal axis) from −300 °C to +100 °C, and start the scale for the volume axis at 0 cm. Draw the best straight line through the data points. Extend a dashed line from the lowest-temperature data point to the left until it intercepts the temperature axis. Note this temperature. It is the temperature at which the height of the air column would, theoretically, be 0 cm; it is absolute zero, or 0 K.

Material Disposal   Your instructor will tell you how to dispose of the materials.

Experiment 13
Prelaboratory Exercises

1. Convert 25 °C to Kelvin.

2. Convert 300 K to degrees Celsius.

3. The average kinetic energy of the particles in a gas increases as the temperature of the gas increases. Explain.

Experiment 13
Laboratory Report

1.

Temperature of water bath °C	Gas volume V (length of air column, cm)	Kelvin temperature T	V/T
_____	_____	_____	_____
_____	_____	_____	_____
_____	_____	_____	_____
_____	_____	_____	_____
_____	_____	_____	_____
_____	_____	_____	_____
_____	_____	_____	_____

2.

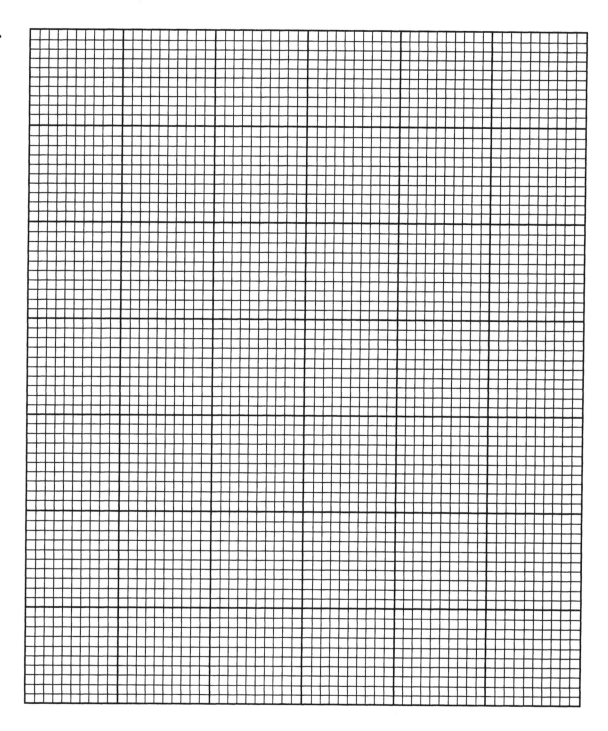

3.

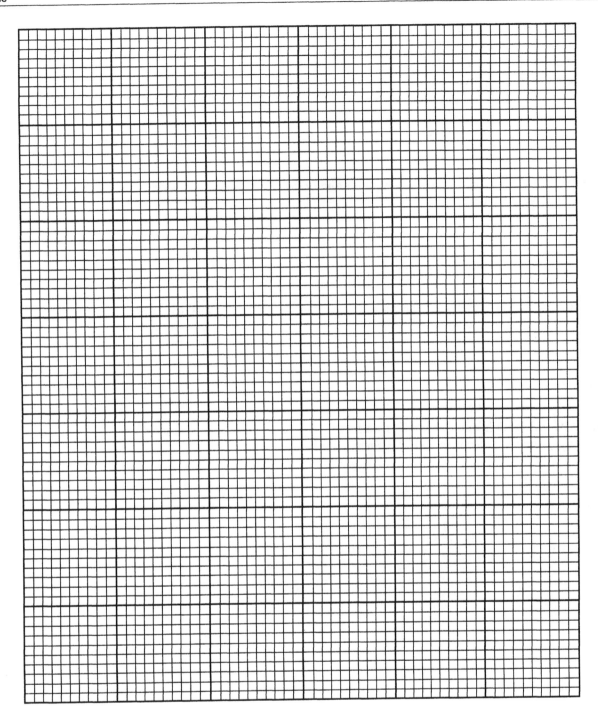

4. Value of absolute zero from graph: _____ °C

Actual value of absolute zero: _____ °C

Postlaboratory Exercise

1. At constant pressure, is the volume of a gas directly proportional to the temperature in degrees Celsius? Explain your answer.

2. How does your experimental value for absolute zero compare with the accepted value? What factors could lead to inaccuracies in your results?

3. How would your results be affected if a very volatile liquid were used as the seal to trap the column of air?

4. A 250-mL sample of air at 50 °C is warmed to 100 °C at constant pressure. What is the volume of the air sample at the new temperature?

Water

Water's polarity is responsible for its remarkable solvent action and helps to explain why ionic compounds such as sodium chloride and copper sulfate and polar covalent compounds such as cane sugar and ammonia dissolve in water. It also explains why nonpolar molecules such as gasoline and oil do not dissolve in water. Water is the medium for many chemical reactions. Most biologically important reactions take place in an aqueous environment.

Hydrogen bonding, the strong attraction of water molecules for each other, is primarily responsible for the unique physical properties of water. These properties include water's high boiling point, high melting point, large heat of vaporization, large heat of fusion, and high surface tension. The large heat of vaporization of water is important to the regulation of our body temperature.

Water is an integral part of many salt crystals. These salts are called *hydrates,* and the water in them is *water of hydration.* Plaster of paris, for example, is the hemihydrate (half-hydrate) of calcium sulfate [$(CaSO_4)_2 \cdot H_2O$]. When treated with water and allowed to set, this compound forms the hard crystalline compound calcium sulfate dihydrate ($CaSO_4 \cdot 2H_2O$). This is the material of the familiar plaster cast.

In this experiment we will examine several of water's interesting properties.

Experiment 14.1   Distillation

Hypothesis

Water can be purified by distillation.

Objective

To distill samples of water that contain volatile and nonvolatile components.

SAFETY PRECAUTIONS	•**Wear safety goggles at all times while in the laboratory.** •**Long hair must be pinned or tied back and loose clothing secured when you are working with flames.** •**Keep flammable substances away from open flames.**

Materials and Equipment

Sodium chloride, dilute ammonia solution, 0.1 M silver nitrate, red food coloring, litmus paper, 250-mL distillation flask, condenser, thermometer, one-hole rubber stopper, dropper pipet, ring stand, ring clamp, wire gauze, laboratory burner, spatula, filter funnel, 100-mL beaker, 100-mL graduated cylinder, medium test tubes, and boiling chips

Procedure

In distillation, a liquid is separated from a mixture by evaporating it, condensing the vapors, and collecting the condensed liquid.

Set up the distillation apparatus shown in Figure 14.1.

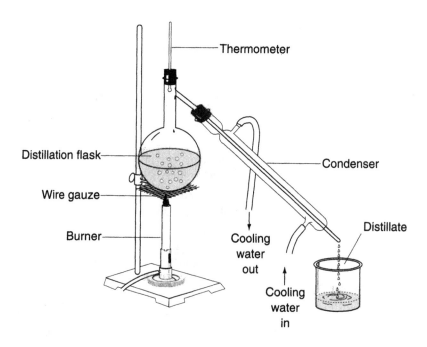

Figure 14.1 *Distillation apparatus.*

1. Dissolve about 1 g of sodium chloride in 100 mL of water, add about 20 drops of red food coloring, and place this solution in the distillation flask. ***Caution: Add a few boiling chips to the solution to prevent it from "bumping" as it begins to boil.*** Position a clean 100-mL beaker to catch the distillate. Pass cold water through the condenser. Heat the contents of the flask, and note the temperature where the water distills. Collect about 10 mL of distillate, and note its color. Test a 3-mL portion of the distillate for chloride ions by adding 5 drops of 0.1 *M* silver nitrate. Test another portion of the distillate with red litmus paper.

2. Turn off the burner, and allow the contents of the flask to cool for about 10 minutes. Remove the thermometer and stopper. Using a long-stemmed funnel, carefully pour about 5 mL of ammonia solution directly into the mixture in the flask. It is important that none of the ammonia solution runs down the sidearm into the condenser. Replace the thermometer, and reheat the contents of the flask. Note the temperature at which the water distills. Collect about 10 mL of distillate in a clean 100-mL beaker. Cautiously smell the distillate, and test a portion of it with red litmus paper. For comparison carefully check the odor of the ammonia solution (***Caution: Ammonia is a choking gas***), and test a portion of it with red litmus paper. Report your results in the data table.

3. Continue the distillation. Discard the next 25 to 30 mL of distillate, and then collect a 5-mL portion in a clean test tube. Check the odor cautiously, and test it with litmus paper. Report your results in the data table.

Material Disposal   Your instructor will tell you how to dispose of the materials.

Experiment 14.2   Solvent Properties of Water

Hypothesis   Water is a solvent for ionic and polar compounds.

Objective   To test the water solubility of some compounds.

SAFETY PRECAUTIONS	• Wear safety goggles at all times while in the laboratory. • Some of the liquids used in this experiment are flammable. Although the volumes used are small, the danger of fire exists. Keep all liquids away from open flames.

Materials and Equipment   Sodium chloride, toluene, glycerol, sucrose, iron(II) sulfate, calcium carbonate, hexane, ammonium nitrate, ethanol, spatula, dropper pipet, and medium test tubes

Procedure   Test each of the substances listed in the data table for water solubility. Use 3 to 4 mL of water in a medium test tube. Add a very small quantity of the substance being tested. The amount should be less than the size of a match head if the substance is a solid or one drop if it is a liquid. Shake the test tube gently, and note what happens. If all the substance dissolves, add another small quantity, and shake gently. Repeat the process several more times if the material is very soluble. In the data table report each substance as *insoluble, slightly soluble,* or *very soluble.*

Material Disposal   Your instructor will tell you how to dispose of the materials.

Experiment 14.3   Water of Hydration

Hypothesis   Water is an integral part of the crystals of many salts.

Objective   To study the composition of some hydrates.

SAFETY PRECAUTIONS	• Wear safety goggles at all times while in the laboratory. • Long hair must be pinned or tied back and loose clothing secured when you are working with flames. • Keep flammable substances away from open flames.

Materials and Equipment   Copper sulfate pentahydrate, sodium chloride, magnesium sulfate heptahydrate, sodium carbonate decahydrate, medium test tubes, test tube holder, laboratory burner, and wire gauze

Procedure   Label four clean, dry test tubes, and place them in a rack. Add small amounts (about 0.3 g) of the following substances: copper sulfate crystals to tube 1, sodium chloride crystals to tube 2, magnesium sulfate crystals to tube 3, and sodium carbonate crystals to tube 4. Holding each test tube horizontally, gently heat the *bottom* of the tube in a burner flame. Report what you see in the upper cooler part of the test tube, and note any change in the appearance of the crystals during heating.

Material Disposal   Your instructor will tell you how to dispose of the materials.

Experiment 14.4   Surface Tension of Water

Hypothesis

The surface of water acts as a membrane.

Objectives

1. To demonstrate the existence of a skin-like membrane on the surface of water owing to surface tension.
2. To study the effect of surface-active agents on the surface tension of water.

SAFETY PRECAUTION	• **Wear safety goggles at all times while in the laboratory.**

Materials and Equipment

Powdered sulfur, 0.1% sodium chloride, 0.1% soap solution (made from bar soap), 0.1% detergent solution (made from a liquid detergent), 0.1% detergent solution (made from a powder detergent), medium test tubes, and test tube rack

Procedure

Clean five medium test tubes, and rinse them thoroughly first with tap water and then with high-purity water to remove all traces of soap or detergent. Set them in the test tube rack. Put about 5 mL of the following liquids into separate test tubes: distilled water, 0.1% sodium chloride solution, 0.1% soap solution, 0.1% liquid detergent solution, 0.1% powder detergent solution. Carefully dust a very small quantity of powdered sulfur onto the surface of each liquid. Record your observations, as you gently tap the tubes, in the data table.

Material Disposal

Your instructor will tell you how to dispose of the materials.

Experiment 14.5   Heat of Fusion of Ice

Hypothesis

The absorption of heat by ice as it melts can be used to cool water, and the extent of the cooling depends on the heat of fusion of ice.

Objective

To determine the heat of fusion of ice.

SAFETY PRECAUTIONS	• **Wear safety goggles at all times while in the laboratory.** • **Long hair must be pinned or tied back and loose clothing secured when you are working with flames.** • **Keep flammable substances away from open flames.**

Materials and Equipment

Ice, Styrofoam cup, thermometer, 100-mL graduated cylinder, 250-mL beaker, laboratory burner, tripod, and wire gauze

Procedure

Water has the largest heat of vaporization of any known liquid. Because of the extensive network of hydrogen bonds in water, it takes 540 cal to change 1 g of water at 100 °C into steam at the same temperature. Therefore, when water as perspiration evaporates from the skin, a large amount of body heat is absorbed to change the water from the liquid to the vapor state. Since this heat comes from the body, the body becomes cooler. Similarly, water has a high heat of fusion. The heat of fusion is the energy required to convert a substance from a solid to a liquid at the melting point of the substance.

Heat 100 mL of water in a 250-mL beaker to about 60 °C. Pour 20 to 30 mL of the hot water into a 100-mL graduated cylinder. After 30 seconds, pour the water out. Repeat this procedure to raise the temperature of the cylinder closer to the temperature of the water. Now add about 30 mL of hot water to the warm cylinder, and insert a thermometer. Half-fill a Styrofoam cup with ice cubes. Quickly drain any excess water from the ice cubes, read the temperature and volume of the hot water in the 100-mL graduated cylinder, and pour this water onto the ice cubes. Stir the ice water rapidly but carefully, until the temperature falls to about 2 °C, but do not allow all the ice to melt. It is important that some ice remain. After noting the final temperature, immediately drain the water from the ice into the 100-mL graduated cylinder. Record the volume of water in the cylinder.

Material Disposal   Your instructor will tell you how to dispose of the materials.

Experiment 14
Prelaboratory Exercises

1. Draw the Lewis dot structure for a water molecule, and explain why the molecule is polar.

2. What is the meaning of the saying, "like dissolves like"?

3. Show how hydrogen bonding occurs between water molecules.

4. In what ways do water molecules at the surface of water differ from water molecules in the bulk of the liquid? What property of water does this difference give rise to?

5. Calculate the mass of water in 1 mol of copper sulfate pentahydrate ($CuSO_4 \cdot 5H_2O$).

6. Explain why ice is less dense than water.

7. Give the freezing point and boiling point of water in Kelvin.

Experiment 14.1 Distillation
Laboratory Report

1. Temperature at which the solution distilled: _____ °C

Color of mixture in flask: _____

Color of distillate : _____

Test for chloride ions in distillate: _____

Red litmus paper test on distillate: _____

2. Temperature at which the solution distilled: _____ °C

Observations

Test	Distillate	Ammonia solution
Odor	_____	_____
	_____	_____
	_____	_____
Red litmus paper	_____	_____
	_____	_____
	_____	_____

3. Odor of distillate: _____

Red litmus paper test: _____

Postlaboratory Exercises

1. Is the red food coloring volatile? What evidence do you have to support your answer?

2. Is sodium chloride volatile? Explain.

3. You have a sample of water that is contaminated with ammonia. Can ammonia-free water be prepared by distillation? Explain your answer.

4. What conclusion can you draw from the odor of the first distillate and the odor of the later distillate of the mixture containing ammonia?

Experiment 14.2   Solvent Properties of Water
Laboratory Report

Substance	Chemical formula	Physical state	Solubility in water
Sodium chloride	_____	_____	_____
Toluene	_____	_____	_____
Glycerol	_____	_____	_____
Sucrose (cane sugar)	_____	_____	_____
Iron(II) sulfate	_____	_____	_____
Calcium carbonate	_____	_____	_____
Hexane	_____	_____	_____
Ammonium nitrate	_____	_____	_____
Ethanol (grain alcohol)	_____	_____	_____

Postlaboratory Exercises

1. Calcium carbonate is an ionic compound. How do you account for the result of the water-solubility test?

2. Which of the liquid substances are (a) the most polar and (b) the most nonpolar?

3. Which of the substances you tested is the most soluble ionic compound?

Experiment 14.3   Water of Hydration

Laboratory Report

Substance	Observations
1. Copper sulfate crystals	_____
	_____
	_____
2. Sodium chloride crystals	_____
	_____
	_____
3. Magnesium sulfate crystals	_____
	_____
	_____
4. Sodium carbonate crystals	_____
	_____
	_____

Postlaboratory Exercises

1. What is the liquid that condenses in the upper part of some of the test tubes?

2. Which of the crystals contained water of hydration?

3. Write an equation for the decomposition of sodium carbonate decahydrate by heat.

4. Barium chloride forms a dihydrate. Write the formula for this compound. Calculate the mass percent composition of water in barium chloride dihydrate.

Experiment 14.4 Surface Tension of Water
Laboratory Report

Liquid	*Observations*
1. Distilled water	_____
	_____
	_____
2. 0.1% Sodium chloride	_____
	_____
	_____
3. 0.1% Soap solution	_____
	_____
	_____
4. 0.1% Liquid detergent	_____
	_____
	_____
5. 0.1% Powder detergent	_____
	_____
	_____

Postlaboratory Exercises

1. Explain how water molecules at the surface differ from those at the interior of a drop of water.

2. Why does talcum powder float on the surface of water?

3. Which of the substances tested reduced the surface tension of water? What evidence do you have to support your conclusion?

4. Water forms beads on an oily surface, but water containing a detergent spreads out. Explain why this happens.

Experiment 14.5   Heat of Fusion of Ice
Laboratory Report

Initial temperature of water: _____ °C

Final temperature of water: _____ °C

Change in temperature of water: _____ °C

Initial volume of water: _____ mL

Final volume of water: _____ mL

Volume of ice melted: _____ mL

Mass of ice melted (1 mL = 1 g):   _____ g

Calories of heat given up by water = initial volume of water $\times$ change in temperature of water

$$= \underline{\hspace{2cm}} \times \underline{\hspace{2cm}}$$

$$= \underline{\hspace{2cm}} \text{ cal}$$

Calories required to melt 1 g of ice = heat of fusion

$$= \frac{\text{heat given up by water (cal)}}{\text{mass of ice melted (g)}}$$

$$= \frac{\text{cal}}{\text{g}}$$

$$= \underline{\hspace{2cm}} \text{ cal/g}$$

The accepted heat of fusion of ice is _____ cal/g.

Postlaboratory Exercises

1. Compare your experimentally determined value for the heat of fusion of ice with the accepted value. How might you account for any error in your value?

2. Explain why steam at 100 °C causes more serious burns than water at the same temperature.

3. How many (a) calories of heat and (b) joules are required to convert 10 g of ice at 0 °C to steam at 100 °C?

Solutions

Solutions consist of two components: a solute (the material that is dissolved) and a solvent (the dissolving medium). We will concern ourselves mainly with aqueous solutions, that is, solutions where the solvent is water.

The formation of a solution is governed by the nature of both the solute and the solvent. In general, those solutes that are polar molecules or ionic compounds dissolve in the polar solvent water. In contrast, nonpolar solutes such as oils and fats dissolve in nonpolar solvents such as gasoline or benzene. Solutions, like other mixtures, have variable composition but, unlike other mixtures, are homogeneous. If a solute is soluble in a particular solvent, the rate at which the solute dissolves depends on the particle size of the solute, the degree of agitation or stirring, and the temperature of the mixture.

The amount of solute that dissolves in a given amount of solvent is the solute's solubility. In addition to the nature of the solute and solvent, solubility also depends on the temperature of the solution. The solubility of many salts increases with increasing temperature, but the solubility of some decreases. A saturated solution contains as much solute as can dissolve at a given temperature. A solution containing less solute than the corresponding saturated solution is unsaturated, and a solution containing more solute than the corresponding saturated solution is supersaturated. Supersaturated solutions are unstable, and the addition of a solute crystal often causes the excess solute to crystallize. The concentration of a solution expresses the relative amount of dissolved solute. It is commonly given as percent (mass/volume), the number of grams of solute per 100 mL of solution, or molarity, the number of moles of solute per liter of solution.

As a general rule, salts containing the following ions are very soluble in water and form solutions that are 3% (mass/volume) or more in concentration: (1) sodium, potassium, and ammonium salts regardless of the anion, (2) chlorides, except those containing lead, silver, or mercury as the cation, and (3) nitrates and acetates, regardless of the cation.

Experiment 15.1   The Concentration of a Saturated Solution

Hypothesis

A saturated solution contains all the solute it can hold at a given temperature.

Objectives

1. To determine the concentration of a saturated solution.
2. To express the concentration of a saturated solution as percent (mass/volume).

SAFETY PRECAUTIONS

- **Wear safety goggles at all times while in the laboratory.**
- **Long hair must be pinned or tied back and loose clothing secured when you are working with flames.**
- **Keep flammable substances away from open flames.**
- **Use tongs when handling the hot evaporating dish.**

Materials and Equipment	Saturated sodium chloride solution, evaporating dish, balance, and water bath (ring stand, ring clamp, wire gauze, 250-mL beaker, burner)

Procedure	Measure the mass of a clean, dry evaporating dish. Pipet 5 mL of saturated sodium chloride solution into the dish. Determine the mass of the solution and dish. Place the dish on a boiling water bath, and evaporate the sodium chloride solution to dryness. Add water to the beaker as required. The evaporation should take about 30 minutes. Remove the evaporating dish, wipe the outside dry, and place it on wire gauze to cool for 5 to 10 minutes. Measure the mass of the evaporating dish and its contents. (If the residue in the evaporating dish still appears moist, reheat the dish on the boiling water bath. Allow the dish to cool to room temperature before putting it on the balance pan.)

Material Disposal	Your instructor will tell you how to dispose of the materials.

Experiment 15.2   Supersaturation

Hypothesis	A supersaturated solution is unstable.

Objectives	1. To prepare a supersaturated solution.
	2. To show the effect of adding a seed crystal to a supersaturated solution.

SAFETY PRECAUTIONS	• **Wear safety goggles at all times while in the laboratory.**
	• **Long hair must be pinned or tied back and loose clothing secured when you are working with flames.**
	• **Keep flammable substances away from open flames.**
	• **Use a test tube holder when heating the test tube.**

Materials and Equipment	Sodium sulfate decahydrate, medium test tube, test tube rack, burner, test tube holder, and 10-mL graduated cylinder

Procedure	Add about 8 mL of water to about 5 g of sodium sulfate crystals in a clean test tube. Heat the test tube in a burner flame, agitating the mixture gently until all the solid has dissolved. Put the test tube in the rack to cool to room temperature. Be careful not to disturb the test tube or contents while they are cooling. (Crystals should not form in the cooling solution. If they do, you must repeat the heating and cooling.) When the solution has cooled to room temperature, add one small crystal of sodium sulfate. Note what happens. Touch the bottom of the test tube to the palm of your hand. Report your observations.

Material Disposal	Your instructor will tell you how to dispose of the materials.

Experiment 15.3　Factors Affecting the Rate of Solution

Hypothesis

Particle size, stirring, and temperature all affect the rate at which a solute dissolves.

Objective

To test the effect of particle size, stirring, and temperature on the rate of solution formation.

SAFETY PRECAUTIONS	• **Wear safety goggles at all times while in the laboratory.** • **Long hair must be pinned or tied back and loose clothing secured when you are working with flames.** • **Keep flammable substances away from open flames.**

Materials and Equipment

Copper sulfate pentahydrate, sodium chloride, medium test tubes, test tube rack, timer, 100-mL beaker, ice, tripod, wire gauze, laboratory burner, mortar and pestle, and spatula

Procedure

A. Effect of Particle Size and Agitation. Place a crystal of copper sulfate about the size of a small pea in each of the test tubes labeled 1 and 2. Place similar quantities of powdered copper sulfate crystals (grind large crystals) in test tubes labeled 3 and 4. Half-fill each of the four test tubes with water, and place test tubes 1 and 3 in the test tube rack without shaking them. Shake test tubes 2 and 4 at the same time. Note how long it takes for the contents of each of the four tubes to dissolve.

B. Effect of Temperature. To three medium test tubes labeled 1, 2, and 3, add sodium chloride crystals to a depth of about 0.5 cm. Place the test tubes in the test tube rack. Boil about 25 mL of water in a 100-mL beaker. In another beaker add about 10 g of ice to 20 mL of cold water. Half-fill test tube 1 with ice cold water, half-fill test tube 2 with water at room temperature, and carefully half-fill test tube 3 with boiling water. Do not shake the tubes. Record your observations.

Material Disposal

Your instructor will tell you how to dispose of the materials.

Experiment 15.4　Factors Affecting Solubility

Hypothesis

The nature of the solute, solvent, and temperature affects solubility.

Objective

To examine the effect of solute, solvent, and temperature on solubility.

SAFETY PRECAUTIONS	• **Wear safety goggles at all times while in the laboratory.** • **Long hair must be pinned or tied back and loose clothing secured when you are working with flames.** • **Keep flammable substances away from open flames.** • **Some of the liquids used in this experiment are flammable. Although the amounts are small, the danger of fire exists. Keep these liquids away from open flames.**

Materials and Equipment

Sodium chloride, sucrose, corn oil, iodine, toluene, potassium nitrate, small test tubes, test tube rack, spatula, dropper pipet, and water bath (ring stand, ring clamp, wire gauze, 250-mL beaker, burner)

Procedure

A. Effect of Solute and Solvent on Solubility.   Add 5 mL of distilled water to each of five small test tubes. Label the tubes 1 through 5. Add 5 mL of toluene to each of an additional five small test tubes. Number these tubes 6 through 10. The liquids in these 10 test tubes are the solvents in this experiment.

To tubes 1 and 6, add pea-sized amounts of sodium chloride; to tubes 2 and 7, add 2 drops of corn oil; to tubes 3 and 8, add pea-sized amounts of sucrose; and to tubes 4 and 9, add a few small crystals of solid iodine. To tube 5, add 2 drops of toluene, and to tube 10, add 2 drops of water. Gently shake the test tubes, and record your results.

B. Effect of Temperature on Solubility.   Place 3 mL of water in a test tube, and heat it in a boiling water bath. Then add solid potassium nitrate to the hot water in the test tube until no more will dissolve. Add the potassium nitrate in small portions, and shake the tube after each addition. Place the test tube in the rack, and allow it to cool slowly. Record what happens.

Material Disposal

Your instructor will tell you how to dispose of the materials.

Experiment 15

Prelaboratory Exercises

1. If 5 g of sodium chloride is dissolved in 250 mL of solution, what is (a) the percent (mass/volume) and (b) the molarity?

2. What is a saturated solution?

3. Name three factors that determine the rate at which a solute dissolves.

4. Name three factors that determine a solute's solubility.

Experiment 15.1   The Concentration of a Saturated Solution

Laboratory Report

Mass of empty evaporating dish: _____ g

Mass of evaporating dish and saturated solution: _____ g

Mass of evaporating dish and sodium chloride: _____ g

Mass of sodium chloride in the saturated solution: _____ g

Calculate the percent (mass/volume) of the saturated solution. (Show calculations.)

Postlaboratory Exercises

1. Using your experimental results, calculate the molar concentration of saturated sodium chloride.

2. A solution contains 24 g of sodium sulfate in 200 mL of solution. Calculate the percent (mass/volume) and the molarity.

3. If 5.0 g of sodium chloride is dissolved in 20 mL of solution at room temperature, is the solution saturated, supersaturated, or unsaturated?

Experiment 15.2   Supersaturation
Laboratory Report

Observations: _____

_____

_____

_____

_____

_____

_____

_____

_____

_____

_____

Postlaboratory Exercises

1. What is the chemical formula of the sodium sulfate crystals? What type of crystals are they?

2. Was there a change in temperature of the solution after the seed crystal was added to the supersaturated solution?

3. What type of solution is left after the effect caused by the seed crystal is complete?

4. Suggest tests that allow you to distinguish unsaturated, saturated, and supersaturated solutions.

Experiment 15.3 Factors Affecting the Rate of Solution

Laboratory Report

A. Tube	Sample and conditions	Time to dissolve, seconds	Observations and comments
1	Large crystal, not shaken	_____	_____
2	Large crystal, shaken	_____	_____
3	Fine crystals, not shaken	_____	_____
4	Fine crystals, shaken	_____	_____

B. Tube	Test conditions	Observations
1	_____	_____
		_____
2	_____	_____
		_____
3	_____	_____
		_____

Postlaboratory Exercises

1. What effect does particle size have on the rate at which a solute dissolves?

2. Why does shaking affect the rate of dissolution?

3. Explain the result you obtained in the temperature study in terms of the kinetic-molecular theory.

Experiment 15.4   Factors Affecting Solubility
Laboratory Report

A. Tube	Solvent	Solute	Observations
1			
2			
3			
4			
5			
6			
7			
8			
9			
10			

B. Observations: _____

_____

_____

_____

_____

_____

_____

_____

Postlaboratory Exercises

1. On the basis of your studies, which solutes would you classify as nonpolar?

2. Why can a substance be a solvent in one system and a solute in another?

3. What is the name of a solution that contains the maximum amount of solute at a given temperature?

4. What can you say about the solubility of potassium nitrate from your experimental observations?

Electrolytes and Nonelectrolytes

Electrolytes are substances that dissolve in water to produce solutions that conduct an electric current. Solutions of electrolytes conduct electricity because electrolytes ionize in aqueous solution. Electrolytes may be strong or weak. Strong electrolytes are good conductors of electricity because in solution they exist almost entirely as ions. Weak electrolytes are poor conductors of electricity because in solution they are only partially dissociated into ions. Substances that dissolve in water but whose solutions do not conduct electric current are nonelectrolytes. Examples of electrolytes and nonelectrolytes are listed in Table 16.1 on the following page.

Hypothesis

Ions in solution transmit an electric current.

Objectives

1. To test the electrical conductivity of various compounds in solution.
2. To classify several compounds as strong electrolytes, weak electrolytes, or nonelectrolytes.

SAFETY PRECAUTIONS	• **Wear safety goggles at all times while in the laboratory.** • **Hydrochloric acid, glacial acetic acid, and sodium hydroxide are damaging to the skin and clothing. Wash off immediately with water if they are spilled, and inform the instructor.** • **Some of the liquids used in this experiment are flammable. Keep them away from open flames.** • **Make certain that the plug is removed from the electrical outlet before doing any experimental setup.** • **Do not touch the electrodes or dip your fingers into the test solution under any circumstances.**

Materials and Equipment

Conductivity apparatus, 100-mL beaker, 5% sucrose solution, sodium chloride, 5% sodium chloride solution, ethanol, kerosene, 6 *M* hydrochloric acid, 6 *M* sodium hydroxide, glacial acetic acid, 6 *M* acetic acid, and 6 *M* aqueous ammonia

Procedure

The apparatus for determining electrical conductivity is shown in Figure 16.1. *Caution: Make certain that the plug is removed from the outlet and that the switch is in the "off" position except when making a test. Do not touch the electrodes or dip your fingers into the test solution under any circumstances.*

Wash the electrodes with distilled water. Do not permit the electrodes to touch. Use a 100-mL beaker as the container for the test substance. Test each of the substances listed below using a 20-mL portion if the substance is a liquid or a 1-cm depth if the substance is a solid. Do not put the plug in the electrical outlet or turn the switch to "on" until the electrodes are correctly positioned in the test substance. The electrodes should be immersed about 0.5 to 1 cm. As each test is completed, turn the switch off, remove the plug, then remove the sample, and finally rinse and

Table 16.1 **Electrolytes and Nonelectrolytes**

	Electrolytes	
Strong	**Weak**	**Nonelectrolytes**
Sodium chloride, NaCl	Carbonic acid, H_2CO_3	Sucrose, $C_{12}H_{22}O_{11}$
Hydrochloric acid, HCl	Aqueous ammonia, NH_3	Ethanol, C_2H_5OH
Sodium hydroxide, NaOH	Acetic acid, CH_3COOH	Acetone, CH_3COCH_3
Magnesium sulfate, $MgSO_4$		Acetaldehyde, CH_3CHO

dry the electrodes. Strong electrolytes are good electrical conductors and cause the filaments of both bulbs to glow brightly. Weak electrolytes are poor electrical conductors, and the current through them is insufficient to light up both bulbs. With very weak electrolytes, only the filament of the 10-watt bulb glows dimly. If the substance is a nonelectrolyte, the solution is nonconducting, and neither filament glows. Identify each substance tested as a strong electrolyte, weak electrolyte, or nonelectrolyte. Upon completion of the experiment, turn the switch off and unplug the apparatus.

Material Disposal   Your instructor will tell you how to dispose of the materials.

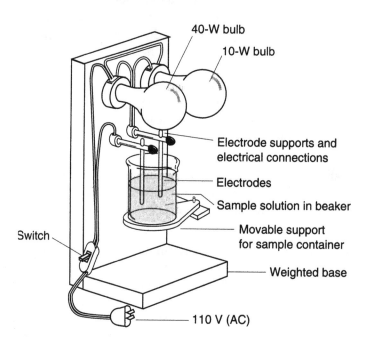

Figure 16.1 Conductivity apparatus.

Experiment 16
Prelaboratory Exercise

1. Which of the following compounds are completely ionized in water?
   (a) HCl   (b) sucrose   (c) acetone   (d) carbonic acid.
   On what evidence do you base your answers?

2. Which of the following solutions is the poorest conductor or a nonconductor of
   electricity? (a) sodium hydroxide   (b) acetic acid   (c) sucrose
   (d) aqueous ammonia

3. It is extremely dangerous to use a hair dryer while sitting in a bath. Why? (*Hint:*
   Tap water contains dissolved salts.)

Experiment 16
Laboratory Report

Substance	Classification	Comments
Distilled water	_____	_____
		_____
Tap water	_____	_____
		_____
5% Sucrose solution	_____	_____
		_____
Ethanol	_____	_____
		_____
Sodium chloride (crystals)		_____
	_____	_____
5% Sodium chloride solution		_____
	_____	_____
Kerosene	_____	_____
		_____
6 M Hydrochloric acid	_____	_____
		_____
6 M Sodium hydroxide	_____	_____
		_____
Glacial acetic acid	_____	_____
		_____
6 M Acetic acid	_____	_____
		_____
6 M Aqueous ammonia	_____	_____

Postlaboratory Exercises

1. For any substances that tested as strong electrolytes, write the formulas of the ions that are present in solution.

2. Compare the conductivity of glacial acetic acid with that of dilute acetic acid. Explain why there is a difference.

3. Sucrose dissolves in water, but its solution does not conduct electricity. Why is sucrose a nonelectrolyte?

4. Compare the conductivities of distilled water and tap water. How can you account for any differences?

5. Why is a solution of sodium chloride very different from sodium chloride crystals in its electrical conductivity?

6. Why is aqueous ammonia only a weak electrolyte?

Acids, Bases, and Salts

As the species that confers acidity to aqueous solutions, the proton is a mediator of life and death. If the acidity of a living system becomes too low or too high, death rapidly occurs. It is therefore important in the biological sciences to understand the fundamental principles of acid-base chemistry and how acidity may be controlled.

The Brønsted-Lowry theory defines acids as substances that are proton donors and bases as proton acceptors. Acids and bases may be strong or weak depending on their degree of ionization. Strong acids and strong bases are completely or almost completely ionized in water, and weak acids and weak bases are only partially ionized. Hydrochloric, nitric, and sulfuric acids are strong acids. Sulfurous, carbonic, and acetic acids are weak acids. Thus hydrochloric acid is completely ionized in water; that is,

$$HCl(aq) + H_2O(l) \longrightarrow H_3O^+(aq) + Cl^-(aq)$$

but carbonic acid is only partially ionized, as shown by the equilibrium expression:

$$H_2CO_3 + H_2O \rightleftharpoons H_3O^+ + HCO_3^-$$

The strong bases include sodium hydroxide and potassium hydroxide; the weak bases include aqueous ammonia (ammonium hydroxide) and sodium bicarbonate. Sodium hydroxide is completely ionized in water.

$$NaOH(aq) \longrightarrow Na^+(aq) + OH^-(aq)$$

Ammonia is only partially ionized in water.

$$NH_3(aq) + H_2O(l) \rightleftharpoons NH_4^+(aq) + OH(aq)^-$$

Acids react with many metals to produce hydrogen gas and a salt.

$$2HCl(aq) + Zn(s) \longrightarrow ZnCl_2(aq) + H_2(g)$$

Acids react with bases to form salts and water in neutralization reactions.

$$HCl(aq) + NaOH(aq) \longrightarrow NaCl(aq) + H_2O(l)$$
$$\text{Acid} \qquad \text{Base} \qquad \text{Salt} \qquad \text{Water}$$

When the base is a carbonate or bicarbonate, carbon dioxide, water, and a salt are produced.

$$2HCl(aq) + Na_2CO_3(aq) \longrightarrow 2NaCl(aq) + H_2O(l) + CO_2(g)$$
$$HCl(aq) + NaHCO_3(aq) \longrightarrow NaCl(aq) + H_2O(l) + CO_2(g)$$

An aqueous solution is acidic, basic, or neutral depending on the molar hydrogen ion concentration ($[H^+]$ or $[H_3O^+]$). Hydrogen ion concentration is conveniently expressed by the pH scale. When $[H^+]$ is $1 \times 10^7 \ M$, it is equal to $[OH^-]$, the solution is neutral, and the pH is 7. A solution with a pH less than 7 is acidic; the lower the pH, the more acidic is the solution. A solution with a pH greater than 7 is basic;

163

the higher the pH, the more basic is the solution. Although acid-base indicators can be used to measure pH, accurate measurements require a pH meter.

In this experiment you will investigate the behavior of some acids and bases in aqueous solution.

Experiment 17.1   The Detection of Acids and Bases

Hypothesis

Certain dyes, called *acid-base indicators* or *pH indicators,* change color as pH changes.

Objectives

1. To observe the effects of acids and bases on several acid-base indicators.
2. To use acid-base indicators to estimate the pH of solutions.

SAFETY PRECAUTIONS	• **Wear safety goggles at all times while in the laboratory.** • **Dilute acids and bases can be damaging to the skin and clothing. Wash off immediately with water if they are spilled, and inform the instructor.**

Materials and Equipment

Dropper bottles filled with indicator solutions (methyl red, litmus, bromthymol blue, phenolphthalein), 0.1 M hydrochloric acid, 0.1 M acetic acid, 0.1 M ammonia, 0.1 M sodium hydroxide, small test tubes, test tube rack, some common household substances and solutions: lemon juice, vinegar, bleach, baking soda (5%), household ammonia, carbonated beverage, shampoo (5%), cold tea, and aspirin tablets

Procedure

Many acid-base indicators are weak acids whose degree of dissociation depends on the pH of the solution. For the general indicator H*In,* the dissociation is

$$H\mathit{In} \rightleftharpoons H^+ + \mathit{In}^-$$

Acid form   Base form

The acid or un-ionized form (H*In*) of an indicator is a different color from the base or ionized form (*In*$^-$). In acidic solution, the equilibrium shifts to the left, and the acid color of the indicator is seen; in basic solution, the equilibrium shifts to the right, and another color of the indicator is observed. The color changes and pH ranges (the ranges in which the indicators change from one color to another) of the indicators used in this experiment are listed below for reference:

Indicator	Color in acid (H*In* form)	Color in base (*In*$^-$ form)	pH Range
Methyl red	Red	Yellow	4.8–6.0
Litmus	Red	Blue	5.2–7.5
Bromthymol blue	Yellow	Blue	6.0–7.6
Phenolphthalein	Colorless	Pink	8.2–10.0

Place 1 or 2 mL of the following liquids in five separate small test tubes: 0.1 M hydrochloric acid, 0.1 M acetic acid, high-purity water, 0.1 M aqueous ammonia, and 0.1 M sodium hydroxide. The test tubes do not have to be dry, but they must be rinsed with high-purity water. Add two drops of methyl red indicator solution to each tube, and then shake to mix the contents. Record the final color and estimated pH. Repeat the procedure for each of the other indicators named in the report table. (Some of the indicators may be available to you only as paper strips. In this case, you should use a strip 2 to 3 cm long. Transfer a drop of the solution to be tested to the indicator paper using a clean glass rod.)

Some of the following common household substances will be available for you to test with pH indicators: lemon juice, vinegar, bleach, baking soda, household ammonia, shampoo, carbonated beverage, cold tea, and an aspirin tablet (suspend in 25 mL of water). After you have tested these substances, you may be asked to check the estimated pH values with a pH meter.

Material Disposal Your instructor will tell you how to dispose of the materials.

Experiment 17.2 Reactions of Acids

Hypothesis
1. Acids react with some metals to produce hydrogen.
2. Acids react with carbonates and bicarbonates to produce carbon dioxide.

Objectives
1. To treat several different metals with acid and test for hydrogen gas.
2. To treat a carbonate and bicarbonate with acid and test for carbon dioxide.

SAFETY PRECAUTIONS	• Wear safety goggles at all times while in the laboratory. • Long hair must be pinned or tied back and loose clothing secured when you are working with flames. • Keep flammable substances away from open flames. • Hydrochloric acid is damaging to the skin and clothing. Wash off immediately with water if it is spilled, and inform the instructor.

Materials and Equipment Iron wire, copper wire, zinc sheet metal, magnesium ribbon, 6 M hydrochloric acid, sodium bicarbonate, calcium carbonate, small test tubes, test tube rack, wood splints, and laboratory burner

Procedure Add 2 mL of 6 M hydrochloric acid to each of six labeled test tubes. To test tube 1, add a 2-cm length of iron wire or a small nail; to test tube 2, add a 2-cm length of copper wire; to test tube 3, add a 2-cm length of magnesium ribbon; to test tube 4, add a small square of zinc sheet metal; to test tube 5, add a small quantity of sodium bicarbonate; and to test tube 6, add a small piece of calcium carbonate. Put the test tubes in a rack, and observe them for a few minutes to see whether a gas is evolved. Test the gas evolved by holding a lighted match or burning splint at the mouth of each test tube. If no gas is evolved, warm the mixture gently in a burner flame (but do not boil) before holding a lighted match at the end of the test tube. Record your results and observations.

Material Disposal Your instructor will tell you how to dispose of the materials.

Experiment 17.3 Neutralization Reactions

Hypothesis An acid reacts with a base to produce a salt.

Objective To produce a salt by neutralization of a base by an acid.

SAFETY PRECAUTIONS

- Wear safety goggles at all times while in the laboratory.
- Long hair must be pinned or tied back and loose clothing secured when you are working with flames.
- Keep flammable substances away from open flames.
- Hydrochloric acid and sodium hydroxide are damaging to the skin and clothing. Wash off immediately with water if they are spilled, and inform the instructor.

Materials and Equipment Hydrochloric acid solution, sodium hydroxide solution, phenolphthalein indicator, 10-mL graduated cylinder, 50-mL beaker, evaporating dish, glass stirring rod, and water bath (ring stand, ring clamp, wire gauze, 250-mL beaker, burner)

Procedure Use a 10-mL graduated cylinder to measure 5 mL of the sodium hydroxide solution into a small beaker. Add 1 to 2 drops of phenolphthalein indicator solution. To this solution add hydrochloric acid dropwise while stirring until the deep pink color *just* disappears. Transfer 4 to 5 mL of this solution to a clean evaporating dish, and evaporate it to dryness over a boiling water bath. Examine and describe the appearance of the residue.

Material Disposal Your instructor will tell you how to dispose of the materials.

Experiment 17
Prelaboratory Exercises

1. Would you describe a weak acid such as acetic acid as a strong electrolyte, weak electrolyte, or nonelectrolyte? Explain.

2. Which solution has the greatest hydrogen ion concentration, (a) 0.1 M hydrochloric acid, (b) 0.1 M acetic acid, (c) 0.1 M sodium hydroxide, or (d) 0.1 M aqueous ammonia? Explain.

3. Which of the solutions in Exercise 2 has the lowest hydrogen ion concentration? Explain.

4. Which of the solutions in Exercise 2 has (a) the highest pH? (b) the lowest pH?

5. What is the definition of pH?

6. Write an equation for the quantitative relationship between [H$^+$] and [OH$^-$] in aqueous solutions.

7. A solution of HCl is 0.01 M. What are the [H$^+$] and pH of this solution? Show calculations.

8. What are the [H$^+$] and pH of 0.01 M NaOH?

Experiment 17.1 The Detection of Acids and Bases

Laboratory Report

1.

	Indicator			
Solution tested	Methyl red	Litmus	Bromthymol blue	Phenolphthalein
1. 0.1 M HCl	_____	_____	_____	_____
2. 0.1 M Acetic acid	_____	_____	_____	_____
3. High-purity water	_____	_____	_____	_____
4. 0.1 M Ammonia	_____	_____	_____	_____
5. 0.1 M NaOH	_____	_____	_____	_____

2.

	Indicator					
Substance tested	Methyl red	Litmus	Bromthymol blue	Phenolphthalein	Estimated pH	Determined pH (meter)
1 _____	_____	_____	_____	_____	_____	_____
2 _____	_____	_____	_____	_____	_____	_____
3 _____	_____	_____	_____	_____	_____	_____
4 _____	_____	_____	_____	_____	_____	_____
5 _____	_____	_____	_____	_____	_____	_____

Postlaboratory Exercises

1. Is the pH of 0.1 M acetic acid equal to, greater than, or less than the pH of 0.1 M hydrochloric acid? Explain.

2. How is a neutral solution defined?

3. What distinguishes an acidic solution from a basic solution?

Experiment 17.2 Reactions of Acids
Laboratory Report

Substance tested	Observations and results
Iron	_____
	_____
	_____
Copper	_____
	_____
	_____
Magnesium	_____
	_____
	_____
Zinc	_____
	_____
	_____
Sodium bicarbonate	_____
	_____
	_____
Calcium carbonate	_____
	_____
	_____

Postlaboratory Exercises

1. Which metals reacted with hydrochloric acid at room temperature to produce hydrogen gas?

2. What evidence do you have to show that hydrogen gas was produced?

3. Arrange the metals in order of increasing reactivity with hydrochloric acid.

4. Which metal(s) required heating in order for reaction to occur?

5. Write a balanced equation for the reaction of the most reactive metal with hydrochloric acid.

6. What gas was given off when sodium bicarbonate was added to hydrochloric acid? What was the evidence of that gas?

7. Write a balanced equation for the reaction of calcium carbonate and hydrochloric acid.

Experiment 17.3 Neutralization Reactions
Laboratory Report

Description of the residue in the evaporating dish:

_____

_____

_____

_____

_____

Postlaboratory Exercises

1. What is the product of the neutralization? How does it compare with the commercial product?

2. Write a balanced equation for the acid-base reaction.

3. What is the name and formula of the salt produced in the neutralization of sulfuric acid by potassium hydroxide? Write a balanced equation for the reaction.

Salt Hydrolysis and Buffer Solutions

Salts formed in the neutralization of a strong acid by a strong base give solutions with a pH of 7. The salt of a weak acid and a strong base gives a basic solution in water. The salt of a strong acid and a weak base gives an acidic solution in water. For example, the salt sodium bicarbonate is the product of a strong base, sodium hydroxide, and a weak acid, carbonic acid. In aqueous solution, the bicarbonate ion (the ion derived from a weak acid) hydrolyzes water to form un-ionized carbonic acid and hydroxide ions.

$$HCO_3^-(aq) + H_2O(l) \rightleftharpoons H_2CO_3(aq) + OH^-(aq)$$

As a result of this equilibrium reaction, the hydroxide ion concentration in solution increases, and therefore, the hydrogen ion concentration must decrease. Consequently, the solution is basic with a pH greater than 7.

Salts that hydrolyze water play an important role in buffer systems. Buffers consist of solutions of a weak acid and a salt of the weak acid or of a weak base and a salt of the weak base. Buffers maintain a relatively constant pH when limited amounts of acid or base are added to solutions containing them. An important buffer in the blood is the carbonic acid–bicarbonate system. This buffer helps to keep the pH of the blood between 7.35 and 7.45. The reactions that buffer against the added acid or base are

$$HCO_3^-(aq) + H^+(aq) \rightleftharpoons H_2CO_3(aq)$$

$$H_2CO_3(aq) + OH^-(aq) \longrightarrow HCO_3^-(aq) + H_2O(l)$$

In this experiment you will measure the pH of solutions of some hydrolyzing salts and examine the effectiveness of buffers against changes in pH.

Experiment 18.1   Salt Hydrolysis

Hypothesis A solution of a salt of a weak acid and a strong base or of a salt of a strong acid and a weak base is not neutral.

Objective To measure the pH of solutions of various salts.

SAFETY PRECAUTION • Wear safety goggles at all times while in the laboratory.

Materials and Equipment Boiled high-purity water, sodium chloride, sodium acetate, ammonium chloride, sodium carbonate, sodium bicarbonate, sodium phosphate, test tubes, dropper pipet, spatula, test tube rack, and wide-range pH paper or indicator solution

Place small quantities (about 0.1 g) of the following salts in separate labeled test tubes: sodium chloride, sodium acetate, ammonium chloride, sodium carbonate, sodium bicarbonate, and sodium phosphate. (The test tubes need not be dry, but they must be well rinsed with high-purity water.) Add 4 to 5 mL of cooled, boiled high-purity water to each tube, and shake gently to dissolve the sample. (If boiled high-purity water is not supplied, you must make your own. Boil some high-purity water in an Erlenmeyer flask for several minutes to expel dissolved carbon dioxide. Then allow the water to cool to room temperature.) Use 2 drops of wide-range indicator solution or small pieces of wide-range pH test paper to measure the pH of each solution and of the boiled high-purity water. Record the pH values.

Material Disposal

Your instructor will tell you how to dispose of the materials.

Experiment 18.2　Buffers

Hypothesis

A buffer solution resists changes in pH.

Objective

To observe the pH changes as acids and bases are added to unbuffered and buffered solutions.

SAFETY PRECAUTIONS	• **Wear safety goggles at all times while in the laboratory.** • **Hydrochloric acid and sodium hydroxide are damaging to the skin and clothing. Wash off immediately with water if they are spilled, and inform the instructor.**

Materials and Equipment

0.1 M sodium carbonate, 0.1 M sodium bicarbonate, 0.1 M sodium monohydrogen phosphate, 0.1 M sodium dihydrogen phosphate, wide-range indicator solution, 1 M hydrochloric acid, 1 M sodium hydroxide, glass stirring rod, medium test tubes, and test tube rack

Procedure

Mix 5 mL of 0.1 M sodium carbonate (Na_2CO_3) and 5 mL of a 0.1 M sodium bicarbonate ($NaHCO_3$) in a small beaker. This is a CO_3^{2-}/HCO_3^- buffer. Label seven test tubes. Divide the solution equally between test tubes 1 and 2. Mix 5 mL of 0.1 M sodium monohydrogen phosphate (Na_2HPO_4) and 5 mL of 0.1 M sodium dihydrogen phosphate (NaH_2PO_4). This is an $HPO_4^{2-}/H_2PO_4^-$ buffer. Divide this solution equally between test tubes 3 and 4. Put 5 mL of 0.1 M $NaHCO_3$ in test tube 5, 5 mL of 0.1 M NaH_2PO_4 in test tube 6, and 5 mL of cooled, boiled high-purity water in test tube 7.

Add *3 drops* of wide-range indicator solution to each of the tubes. Estimate the pH of each solution by comparing your result and the color chart supplied with the indicator. Record your results in the data table.

Add *1 drop* of 1 M hydrochloric acid to tubes 1, 3, 5, 6, and 7. Shake the solutions, note the color changes, and estimate the pH. Record your results.

Add *2 drops* of 1 M sodium hydroxide to the tubes that received the hydrochloric acid, shake the solutions, and again estimate the pH.

If time permits, you can add more hydrochloric acid to tubes 1 and 3, dropwise and with stirring, until the pH falls to about 2. Record the number of drops.

Material Disposal

Your instructor will tell you how to dispose of the materials.

Experiment 18
Prelaboratory Exercises

1. Name two weak acids and two weak bases.

2. Name two kinds of compounds that react to give a salt whose aqueous solution is basic.

3. The pH of a solution is 8. What is $[H^+]$ and $[OH^-]$ in this solution?

4. What are the products of the reaction between nitric acid and aqueous ammonia?

5. If the salt produced in Exercise 4 is dissolved in water, will the solution be acidic, neutral, or basic?

Experiment 18.1   Salt Hydrolysis
Laboratory Report

Boiled high-purity water pH: _____

Aqueous solution	Chemical formula	pH
1. Sodium chloride	_____	_____
2. Sodium acetate	_____	_____
3. Ammonium chloride	_____	_____
4. Sodium carbonate	_____	_____
5. Sodium bicarbonate	_____	_____
6. Sodium phosphate	_____	_____

Postlaboratory Exercises

1. Which salts give basic solutions?

2. Name the weak acids from which the salts are derived.

3. Why does NaCl give the pH you obtained?

4. Predict the pH of solutions of the following salts (greater than 7, equal to 7, or less than 7):

(a) $NaNO_3$ _____

(b) Na_2SO_4 _____

(c) $(NH_4)_2SO_4$ _____

(d) K_2CO_3 _____

(e) H_3PO_4 _____

(f) $KHCO_3$ _____

5. Why is it necessary to use boiled high-purity water in this experiment? How might the test results have differed if the high-purity water had not been boiled prior to doing this experiment?

Experiment 18.2   Buffers
Laboratory Report

1.

Tube	Contents of tube	Initial pH	pH after Adding HCl	pH after Adding NaOH
1	CO_3^{2-}/HCO_3^-	_____	_____	_____
2	CO_3^{2-}/HCO_3^-	_____	_____	_____
3	$HPO_4^{2-}/H_2PO_4^-$	_____	_____	_____
4	$HPO_4^{2-}/H_2PO_4^-$	_____	_____	_____
5	$NaHCO_3$	_____	_____	_____
6	NaH_2PO_4	_____	_____	_____
7	Boiled high-purity water	_____	_____	_____

2. Tube 1: _____ drops

Tube 3: _____ drops

Postlaboratory Exercises

1. What was the purpose of adding 2 drops of NaOH to the test solution in the second part of the experiment? What would you have observed if only 1 drop of NaOH had been added?

2. What is the function of a buffer? Does a buffer always maintain a solution at pH 7?

3. Based on your experimental evidence, which buffer system had the greatest buffering capacity?

4. Which solution showed the largest change in pH with the addition of 1 drop of HCl?

5. Write equations for the reaction of the $HPO_4^{2-}/H_2PO_4^-$ buffer with an acid and with a base.

6. Is 0.1 M $NaHCO_3$ a good buffer? Explain.

7. Is 0.1 M NaH_2PO_4 a good buffer? Explain.

CPSIA information can be obtained
at www.ICGtesting.com
Printed in the USA
FFHW022109291218
50017503-54770FF